Extra Practice

Author
Bernice Lau Pui Wah

Marshall Cavendish
Education

U.S. Distributor

Houghton Mifflin Harcourt

© 2015 Marshall Cavendish Education Pte Ltd

Published by Marshall Cavendish Education
An imprint of Marshall Cavendish Education Pte Ltd
Times Centre, 1 New Industrial Road, Singapore 536196
Customer Service Hotline: (65) 6213 9444
US Office Tel: (1-914) 332 8888 Fax: (1-914) 332 8882
E-mail: tmesales@mceducation.com
Website: www.mceducation.com

Distributed by
Houghton Mifflin Harcourt
222 Berkeley Street
Boston, MA 02116
Tel: 617-351-5000
Website: www.hmheducation.com/mathinfocus

First published 2015

Math in Focus® Extra Practice 5A
ISBN 978-0-544-17636-2

Printed in Singapore

2 3 4 5 6 7 8   1401   20 19 18 17 16 15
4500495929   A B C D E

Contents

CHAPTER 1 — Whole Numbers

Lesson 1.1	Numbers to 10,000,000	1
Lesson 1.2	Place Value	5
Lesson 1.3	Comparing Numbers to 10,000,000	9
Lesson 1.4	Rounding and Estimating	11

Put on Your Thinking Cap! — 15

CHAPTER 2 — Whole Number Multiplication and Division

Lesson 2.1	Using a Calculator	17
Lesson 2.2	Multiplying by Tens, Hundreds, or Thousands	19
Lesson 2.3	Multiplying by Powers of Ten	23
Lesson 2.4	Multiplying by 2-Digit Numbers	25
Lesson 2.5	Dividing by Tens, Hundreds, or Thousands	27
Lesson 2.6	Dividing by 2-Digit Numbers	31
Lesson 2.7	Order of Operations	33
Lesson 2.8	Real-World Problems: Multiplication and Division	37

Put on Your Thinking Cap! — 45

Fractions and Mixed Numbers

Lesson 3.1   Adding Unlike Fractions   51
Lesson 3.2   Subtracting Unlike Fractions   53
Lesson 3.3   Fractions, Mixed Numbers, and Division
             Expressions   55
Lesson 3.4   Expressing Fractions, Division Expressions,
             and Mixed Numbers as Decimals   57
Lesson 3.5   Adding Mixed Numbers   59
Lesson 3.6   Subtracting Mixed Numbers   61
Lesson 3.7   Real-World Problems: Fractions and
             Mixed Numbers   63

Put on Your Thinking Cap!   69

Multiplying and Dividing Fractions and Mixed Numbers

Lesson 4.1   Multiplying Proper Fractions   73
Lesson 4.2   Real-World Problems: Multiplying with
             Proper Fractions   75
Lesson 4.3   Multiplying Improper Fractions by Fractions   81
Lesson 4.4   Multiplying Mixed Numbers and Whole Numbers   83
Lesson 4.5   Real-World Problems: Multiplying with
             Mixed Numbers   89
Lesson 4.6   Dividing Fractions and Whole Numbers   91
Lesson 4.7   Real-World Problems: Multiplying and
             Dividing with Fractions   99

Put on Your Thinking Cap!   107

Test Prep for Chapters 1 to 4   113

CHAPTER 5 Algebra

Lesson 5.1	Number Patterns and Relationships	119
Lesson 5.2	Using Letters as Numbers	123
Lesson 5.3	Simplifying Algebraic Expressions	131
Lesson 5.4	Inequalities and Equations	133
Lesson 5.5	Real-World Problems: Algebra	135

Put on Your Thinking Cap!   139

CHAPTER 6 Area

Lesson 6.1	Finding the Area of a Rectangle with Fractional Side Lengths	141
Lesson 6.2	Base and Height of a Triangle	143
Lesson 6.3	Finding the Area of a Triangle	145

Put on Your Thinking Cap!   147

CHAPTER 7 Ratio

Lesson 7.1	Finding Ratio	151
Lesson 7.2	Equivalent Ratios	153
Lesson 7.3	Real-World Problems: Ratios	155
Lesson 7.4	Ratios in Fraction Form	157
Lesson 7.5	Comparing Three Quantities	159
Lesson 7.6	Real-World Problems: More Ratios	161

Put on Your Thinking Cap!   163

Mid-Year Test   167

Answers   179

Introducing

Math in Focus®

Extra Practice

Extra Practice 5A and *5B*, written to complement *Math in Focus®: Singapore Math®* by Marshall Cavendish Grade 5, offer further practice very similar to the Practice exercises in the Student Books and Workbooks for on-level students.

Extra Practice provides ample questions to reinforce all the concepts taught, and includes challenging questions in the Put on Your Thinking Cap! pages. These pages provide extra non-routine problem-solving opportunities, strengthening critical thinking skills.

Extra Practice is an excellent option for homework, or may be used in class or after school. It is intended for students who simply need more practice to become confident, or secure students who are aiming for excellence.

CHAPTER 2 Whole Number Multiplication and Division

Lesson 2.1   Using a Calculator

Use your calculator in this lesson.

Add.

1. $3,857 + 2,684 =$ _____

2. $5,729 + 2,865 =$ _____

3. $1,898 + 4,573 =$ _____

4. $2,948 + 4,676 =$ _____

Subtract.

5. $4,216 - 1,678 =$ _____

6. $5,042 - 1,857 =$ _____

7. $26,111 - 12,935 =$ _____

8. $108,123 - 15,987 =$ _____

Multiply.

9. $268 \times 94 =$ _____

10. $479 \times 58 =$ _____

11. $1,579 \times 48 =$ _____

12. $36,450 \times 28 =$ _____

Divide.

13.   6,356 ÷ 7 = _____

14.   6,344 ÷ 8 = _____

15.   2,632 ÷ 47 = _____

16.   5,796 ÷ 69 = _____

17.   15,696 ÷ 36 = _____

18.   322,077 ÷ 98 = _____

Use your calculator to solve this question.

19.   **Step 1**   Write any whole number between 100 and 999.
         Step 2   Multiply the number by 11.
         Step 3   Then multiply the product by 91.

Repeat the three steps by choosing another number in Step 1.
What do you notice about the answers?

Lesson 2.2   Multiplying by Tens, Hundreds, or Thousands

Multiply.

1. $38 \times 10 =$ _____

2. $746 \times 10 =$ _____

3. $624 \times 10 =$ _____

4. $857 \times 10 =$ _____

5. $758 \times 10 =$ _____

6. $680 \times 10 =$ _____

Find the missing factors.

7. $681 \times$ _____ $= 6,810$

8.   _____ $\times 10 = 1,900$

9. $453 \times$ _____ $= 4,530$

10. $1,905 \times$ _____ $= 19,050$

11.   _____ $\times 10 = 64,000$

12.   _____ $\times 10 = 808,000$

Fill in the blanks.

13. $56 \times 80 = (56 \times$ _____ $) \times 10$

   $=$ _____ $\times 10$

   $=$ _____

14. $756 \times 40 = (756 \times$ _____ $) \times 10$

   $=$ _____ $\times 10$

   $=$ _____

15. $680 \times 50 = (680 \times$ _____ $) \times 10$

$= $ _____ $\times 10$

$= $ _____

16. $857 \times 60 = ($ _____ $\times$ _____ $) \times 10$

$= $ _____ $\times 10$

$= $ _____

Multiply.

17. 38×40 **18.** 572×80

19. 490×30 **20.** 375×70

Multiply.

21. $47 \times 100 = $ _____

22. $325 \times 100 = $ _____

23. $168 \times 100 = $ _____

24. $231 \times 1{,}000 = $ _____

25. $192 \times 1{,}000 = $ _____

26. $759 \times 1{,}000 = $ _____

Fill in the blanks.

27. $386 \times $ _____ $ = 38{,}600$

28. _____ $\times 100 = 712{,}000$

29. $623 \times $ _____ $ = 623{,}000$

30. $816 \times $ _____ $ = 81{,}600$

31. _____ $\times 1{,}000 = 7{,}910{,}000$

32. _____ $\times 1{,}000 = 5{,}200{,}000$

Fill in the blanks.

33. $24 \times 600 = (24 \times $ _____ $) \times 100$

$= $ _____ $\times 100$

$= $ _____

34. $108 \times 400 = (108 \times $ _____ $) \times 100$

$= $ _____ $\times 100$

$= $ _____

35. $160 \times 500 = (160 \times$ _____ $) \times 100$

   $=$ _____ $\times 100$

   $=$ _____

36. $37 \times 3,000 = (37 \times$ _____ $) \times 1,000$

   $=$ _____ $\times 1,000$

   $=$ _____

37. $103 \times 8,000 = (103 \times$ _____ $) \times 1,000$

   $=$ _____ $\times 1,000$

   $=$ _____

38. $325 \times 4,000 = (325 \times$ _____ $) \times 1,000$

   $=$ _____ $\times 1,000$

   $=$ _____

Multiply.

39. 209×700

40. $146 \times 9,000$

Name: _____ Date: _____

Lesson 2.3   Multiplying by Powers of Ten

Multiply.

1. $95 \times 10 =$ _____

$95 \times 10^2 =$ _____ $\times$ _____

$=$ _____

$95 \times 10^3 =$ _____ $\times$ _____

$=$ _____

2. $86 \times 10 =$ _____

$86 \times 10^2 =$ _____ $\times$ _____

$=$ _____

$86 \times 10^3 =$ _____ $\times$ _____

$=$ _____

3. $453 \times 10 =$ _____

$453 \times 10^2 =$ _____ $\times$ _____

$=$ _____

$453 \times 10^3 =$ _____ $\times$ _____

$=$ _____

4. $128 \times 10 =$ _____

$128 \times 10^2 =$ _____ $\times$ _____

$=$ _____

$128 \times 10^3 =$ _____ $\times$ _____

$=$ _____

5. $6{,}250 \times 10 =$ _____

       $6{,}250 \times 10^2 =$ _____ $\times$ _____

              $=$ _____

       $6{,}250 \times 10^3 =$ _____ $\times$ _____

              $=$ _____

6. $9{,}360 \times 10 =$ _____

       $9{,}360 \times 10^2 =$ _____ $\times$ _____

              $=$ _____

       $9{,}360 \times 10^3 =$ _____ $\times$ _____

              $=$ _____

7. $248 \times 3 =$ _____   **8.** $347 \times 5 =$ _____

       $248 \times 30 =$ _____ $347 \times 50 =$ _____

9. $137 \times 4 =$ _____   **10.** $564 \times 8 =$ _____

       $137 \times 400 =$ _____ $564 \times 800 =$ _____

11. $526 \times 6 =$ _____   **12.** $196 \times 9 =$ _____

       $526 \times 6{,}000 =$ _____ $196 \times 9{,}000 =$ _____

Lesson 2.4   Multiplying by 2-Digit Numbers

Multiply. Estimate to check if your answers are reasonable.

1. 46×80

2. 53×90

3. 49×46

4. 58×52

5. 37×63

6. 65×47

7. 86×43

8. 96×84

Multiply. Estimate to check if your answers are reasonable.

9.   763 × 40

10.   370 × 60

11.   495 × 27

12.   856 × 56

13.   1,268 × 39

14.   1,046 × 93

15.   1,203 × 78

16.   3,108 × 24

Lesson 2.5   Dividing by Tens, Hundreds, or Thousands

Divide.

1. $7{,}200 \div 10 =$ _____   **2.** $2{,}800 \div 10 =$ _____

3. $23{,}000 \div 10 =$ _____   **4.** $680{,}000 \div 10 =$ _____

Fill in the blanks.

5. $2{,}320 \div 10 =$ _____

6.   _____ $\div 10 = 160$

7. $24{,}000 \div$ _____ $= 2{,}400$

8. $84{,}000 \div$ _____ $= 8{,}400$

9.   _____ $\div 10 = 398$

10.   _____ $\div 10 = 5{,}500$

Fill in the blanks.

11. $9{,}300 \div 30 = (9{,}300 \div$ _____ $) \div 3$

                 $=$ _____ $\div 3$

                 $=$ _____

12. $9{,}500 \div 50 = (9{,}500 \div 10) \div$ _____

                 $=$ _____ $\div$ _____

                 $=$ _____

13. $126{,}000 \div 60 = (126{,}000 \div 10) \div$ _____

$= \underline{\hspace{2cm}} \div \underline{\hspace{2cm}}$

$= \underline{\hspace{2cm}}$

Divide.

14. $60{,}000 \div 40$ **15.** $372{,}000 \div 60$

16. $486{,}000 \div 90$ **17.** $267{,}400 \div 70$

Divide.

18. $4{,}800 \div 100 =$ _____

19. $35{,}700 \div 100 =$ _____

20. $79{,}000 \div 1{,}000 =$ _____

21. $350{,}000 \div 1{,}000 =$ _____

Name: _____ **Date:** _____

Fill in the blanks.

22. $19{,}200 \div 100 = $ _____

23. _____ $\div\ 100 = 2{,}750$

24. $77{,}000 \div$ _____ $= 770$

25. $930{,}000 \div$ _____ $= 930$

26. _____ $\div\ 1{,}000 = 514$

27. _____ $\div\ 100 = 6{,}800$

Fill in the blanks.

28. $13{,}500 \div 300 = (13{,}500 \div$ _____$) \div 3$

$\qquad\qquad = $ _____ $\div\ 3$

$\qquad\qquad = $ _____

29. $85{,}000 \div 500 = (85{,}000 \div 100) \div$ _____

$\qquad\qquad = $ _____ $\div$ _____

$\qquad\qquad = $ _____

30. $840{,}000 \div 400 = (840{,}000 \div$ _____$) \div 4$

$\qquad\qquad = $ _____ $\div\ 4$

$\qquad\qquad = $ _____

31. $924{,}000 \div 6{,}000 = (924{,}000 \div$ _____$) \div 6$

$\qquad\qquad = $ _____ $\div\ 6$

$\qquad\qquad = $ _____

32. $981,000 \div 9,000 = (981,000 \div 1,000) \div$ _____

$= $ _____ $\div$ _____

$= $ _____

33. $756,000 \div 7,000 = (756,000 \div$ _____ $) \div 7$

$= $ _____ $\div 7$

$= $ _____

Divide.

34. $12,400 \div 400$

35. $456,000 \div 3,000$

Lesson 2.6   Dividing by 2-Digit Numbers

Divide.

1.   80 ÷ 20

2.   100 ÷ 18

3.   130 ÷ 43

4.   620 ÷ 52

5.   198 ÷ 23

6.   240 ÷ 34

7.   624 ÷ 29

8.   831 ÷ 45

Estimate the quotient. Then divide.

9.   3,160 ÷ 40

10.   3,250 ÷ 50

11.   2,566 ÷ 24

12.   3,129 ÷ 38

13.   4,163 ÷ 42

14.   1,986 ÷ 51

15.   1,300 ÷ 49

16.   1,170 ÷ 61

CHAPTER 3

Fractions and Mixed Numbers

Lesson 3.1   Adding Unlike Fractions

Find two equivalent fractions for each fraction.

1. $\frac{1}{4}$ = _____ = _____

2. $\frac{2}{3}$ = _____ = _____

3. $\frac{4}{9}$ = _____ = _____

4. $\frac{3}{5}$ = _____ = _____

5. $\frac{6}{7}$ = _____ = _____

6. $\frac{5}{8}$ = _____ = _____

Shade and label each model to show the fractions. Then complete the addition sentence.

7. $\frac{2}{3}, \frac{1}{4}$

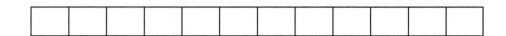

$$\frac{2}{3} + \frac{1}{4} = \text{_____} + \text{_____}$$

$$= \text{_____}$$

8. $\frac{2}{5}, \frac{1}{2}$

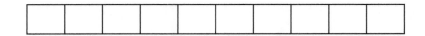

$$\frac{2}{5} + \frac{1}{2} = \text{_____} + \text{_____}$$

$$= \text{_____}$$

Estimate each sum by rounding the fractions to 0, $\frac{1}{2}$, or 1. Then find the actual sum. Express each sum in simplest form.

9. $\frac{2}{5} + \frac{3}{8}$

10. $\frac{1}{3} + \frac{1}{10}$

11. $\frac{7}{10} + \frac{3}{4}$

12. $\frac{4}{5} + \frac{2}{3}$

13. $\frac{7}{8} + \frac{1}{6}$

14. $\frac{6}{7} + \frac{3}{4}$

Lesson 3.2 Subtracting Unlike Fractions

Fill in the blanks.

1. Rewrite the two fractions as like fractions with the same denominator.

$$\frac{4}{5} = \frac{\boxed{}}{\boxed{}}$$

$$\frac{1}{2} = \frac{\boxed{}}{\boxed{}}$$

Using the equivalent fractions, complete the model and the subtraction sentence.

$$\frac{4}{5} = \boxed{}$$

$$\frac{1}{2} = \boxed{}$$

$$\frac{4}{5} - \frac{1}{2} = \boxed{} - \boxed{}$$

$$= \boxed{}$$

2. Rewrite the two fractions as like fractions with the same denominator. Then complete the model and the subtraction sentence.

$$\frac{4}{9} = \boxed{} \qquad\qquad \frac{1}{6} = \boxed{}$$

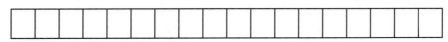

$$\frac{4}{9} - \frac{1}{6} = \underline{\hspace{2cm}} - \underline{\hspace{2cm}} = \underline{\hspace{2cm}}$$

Estimate each difference by rounding the fractions to $0, \frac{1}{2}$, or 1. Then find the actual difference. Express each difference in simplest form.

3. $\frac{4}{5} - \frac{1}{3}$ **4.** $\frac{3}{4} - \frac{2}{3}$

5. $\frac{8}{9} - \frac{7}{8}$ **6.** $\frac{7}{12} - \frac{1}{4}$

7. $\frac{5}{6} - \frac{3}{8}$ **8.** $\frac{8}{9} - \frac{1}{2}$

Lesson 3.3 Fractions, Mixed Numbers, and Division Expressions

Look at each model. Then write each division expression as a fraction and as a mixed number if appropriate.

1.

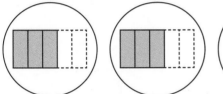 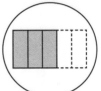 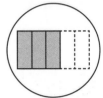

$$3 \div 5 = \dfrac{\boxed{}}{\boxed{}}$$

2.

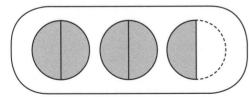 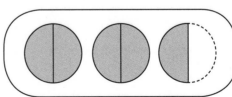

$$5 \div 2 = \dfrac{\boxed{}}{\boxed{}} = \boxed{}\,\dfrac{\boxed{}}{\boxed{}}$$

Write each division expression as a fraction or mixed number in simplest form.

3. 3 ÷ 25

4. 4 ÷ 38

5. 54 ÷ 7

6. 48 ÷ 9

Express each fraction as a mixed number in simplest form.

7. $\frac{18}{4}$

8. $\frac{20}{6}$

9. $\frac{44}{8}$

10. $\frac{42}{9}$

Lesson 3.4   Expressing Fractions, Division Expressions, and Mixed Numbers as Decimals

Rewrite each fraction as a decimal.

1. $\dfrac{9}{10}$

2. $\dfrac{4}{5}$

3. $\dfrac{3}{20}$

4. $\dfrac{9}{25}$

5. $\dfrac{23}{10}$

6. $\dfrac{5}{2}$

7. $\dfrac{11}{4}$

8. $\dfrac{18}{5}$

Express each division expression as a decimal.

9. $17 \div 25$ **10.** $15 \div 4$

Express each mixed number as a decimal.

11. $2\frac{3}{5}$ **12.** $3\frac{7}{8}$

13. $4\frac{7}{20}$ **14.** $5\frac{3}{4}$

Solve. Show your work.

15.   Rayza buys 6 similar notebooks for $15. How much does she pay
          for each notebook?

Lesson 3.7   Real-World Problems: Fractions and Mixed Numbers

Solve. Show your work.

1.   It takes 28 minutes to play 8 songs on a radio. Every song is played for the same length of time. How long does it take to play 1 song? Express your answer as

   a.   a mixed number

   b.   a decimal

2.   At a parade, $\frac{1}{4}$ of the participants have red hair, $\frac{1}{6}$ of them have brown hair, and the rest of the participants have black hair. What fraction of the participants have black hair?

3. Rashan buys $3\frac{7}{10}$ pounds of flour and Diego buys $2\frac{3}{4}$ pounds of flour. They use $4\frac{3}{5}$ pounds of flour to bake bread. How much flour is left? Express your answer as a decimal.

4. Maria uses $2\frac{3}{4}$ meters of cloth to make a dress and $\frac{5}{8}$ meter less cloth to make a blouse. How much cloth does she use in all? Express your answer as a decimal.

5. A carton contains $1\frac{8}{9}$ liters of apple juice. Rosalia drinks $\frac{1}{6}$ liter of the juice every day. How much apple juice is left in the carton after a week?

6. Leena bakes a loaf of bread. She eats $\frac{1}{8}$ of the loaf and gives $\frac{1}{6}$ of it to each of her 3 friends. What fraction of the loaf of bread is left?

7. Thomas reads $\frac{2}{9}$ of a book on Monday and $\frac{1}{6}$ of it on Tuesday. He reads twice as many pages on Wednesday as on Tuesday. What fraction of the book is not read?

8. In a day, Jamal spent $1\frac{2}{3}$ hours watching television, $1\frac{4}{5}$ hours taking an afternoon nap, and $\frac{7}{8}$ hour helping his mother with housework.

    a. How much time did Jamal spend on watching television and helping with housework?

    b. How much more time did Jamal spend taking the nap than helping with housework?

9. Madison buys $2\frac{3}{5}$ pounds of meat. Her neighbor buys $\frac{3}{4}$ pound more meat than Madison. How many pounds of meat do they buy altogether?

10. Box A weighs $1\frac{7}{10}$ pounds. Box B weighs $\frac{1}{4}$ pound less than Box A. What is the total weight of the two boxes?

11. The length of a storeroom is $4\frac{3}{5}$ meters. The storeroom's width is $\frac{3}{4}$ meter shorter than its length. What is the perimeter of the storeroom?

12. John poured $2\frac{1}{2}$ liters of water into a tank. Then he poured out $3\frac{2}{5}$ liters of water from the tank, leaving $4\frac{1}{5}$ liters of water in the tank. How much water was in the tank at first?

 Put on Your Thinking Cap!

Solve. Show your work.

1. Two ropes, P and Q, are each cut into 3 equal pieces. Each piece cut from rope Q is $\frac{2}{5}$ meter longer than each piece cut from rope P. If rope P is 2 meters long, what is the length of rope Q?

2. Lionel has $\frac{3}{4}$ as much money as Gary. Gary has $\frac{1}{3}$ as much money as Vivian. How many times Lionel's amount of money is Vivian's amount of money?

3. Andrew found that $\frac{4}{5}$ of his savings is equal to $\frac{1}{2}$ of Malik's savings. What fraction of Malik's savings is Andrew's savings?

4. Find the value of:

$$\frac{1}{100} + \frac{2}{100} + \frac{3}{100} + \cdots\cdots + \frac{97}{100} + \frac{98}{100} + \frac{99}{100}$$

$$\frac{1}{100} + \frac{99}{100} = 1$$

5. Find the value of:

$$\frac{1}{99} + \frac{2}{99} + \frac{3}{99} + \cdots\cdots + \frac{8}{99} + \frac{9}{99} + \frac{10}{99}$$

6. Find the value of:

$$\frac{1}{1 \times 2} + \frac{1}{2 \times 3} + \frac{1}{3 \times 4} + \cdots\cdots + \frac{1}{28 \times 29} + \frac{1}{29 \times 30}$$

$$\frac{1}{1 \times 2} = \frac{1}{2}$$

$$\frac{1}{2 \times 3} = \frac{1}{6}$$

7. In a class where there are as many girls as boys, $\frac{2}{5}$ of the boys and $\frac{1}{2}$ of the girls went to a local fair. What fraction of the students in the class did not go to the local fair?

8. Alvin has some marbles in a box. He keeps $\frac{1}{3}$ of them and gives the remainder to Joyce and Sean. Joyce gets $\frac{5}{8}$ of the remainder. What fraction of the marbles does Sean get?

Multiplying and Dividing Fractions and Mixed Numbers

Lesson 4.1   Multiplying Proper Fractions

Look at the diagram. Then complete.

1.

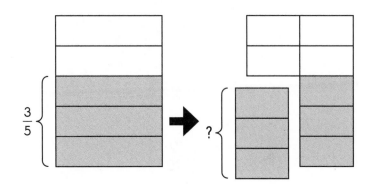

$\frac{1}{2}$ of $\frac{3}{5}$ = $\dfrac{\boxed{}}{\boxed{}}$ × $\dfrac{\boxed{}}{\boxed{}}$

= $\dfrac{\boxed{}}{\boxed{}}$

Complete.

2. $\frac{3}{4}$ of $\frac{5}{7}$ = $\dfrac{\boxed{}}{\boxed{}}$ × $\dfrac{\boxed{}}{\boxed{}}$

= $\dfrac{\boxed{}}{\boxed{}}$

Multiply. Express each product in simplest form.

3. $\frac{5}{6}$ of $\frac{9}{11}$

4. $\frac{7}{10}$ of $\frac{5}{9}$

5. $\frac{7}{8} \times \frac{10}{14}$

6. $\frac{8}{9} \times \frac{9}{10}$

7. $\frac{3}{5} \times \frac{4}{12}$

8. $\frac{5}{7} \times \frac{7}{10}$

Lesson 4.2 Real-World Problems: Multiplying with Proper Fractions

Solve. Show your work.

1. Tian has 56 paper clips. He gives $\frac{3}{4}$ of them to Joe. Joe gives $\frac{2}{7}$ of what he receives to Rahul. How many paper clips does Rahul get?

2. Tony is given $\frac{9}{10}$ hour to mow a lawn. He only uses $\frac{2}{3}$ of the given time to mow the lawn. How much time is left?

3. Keith spends $\frac{1}{6}$ of his savings on a magazine and $\frac{2}{5}$ of the remainder on a book. What fraction of his savings is left?

4. There are some hats in a box. $\frac{1}{6}$ of them are red, $\frac{1}{3}$ are blue, and $\frac{3}{7}$ of the remainder are green. If there are 27 green hats, how many hats are there altogether?

5. Lily receives 30 messages on her cell phone. Of those messages, $\frac{1}{5}$ are picture messages and $\frac{7}{8}$ of the remainder are text messages. How many text messages does she receive?

6. Sam makes some bread rolls. He gives $\frac{2}{5}$ of the bread rolls to his neighbor and $\frac{4}{9}$ of the remainder to his cousin. He has 15 bread rolls left. How many bread rolls does Sam make?

7. Anne has 24 more cards than Devi. Anne finds that $\frac{3}{5}$ of Devi's cards are equal to $\frac{1}{2}$ of her cards. How many cards does Anne have?

8. Roxanne has $\frac{1}{2}$ as many beads as Sherie. The number of beads Sherie has is $\frac{4}{5}$ that of Marcos. Marcos has 165 beads. How many more beads does Marcos have than Roxanne?

9.   Ken spends $\frac{1}{5}$ of his money on a dictionary. He gives $21 to his brother and has $\frac{1}{2}$ of his money left. How much money does Ken have left?

10.   Victoria spends $\frac{5}{9}$ of her money on a chicken pie and two ears of corn. Each ear of corn costs $\frac{1}{6}$ as much as the chicken pie. Victoria has $24 left.

    a.   How much does Victoria spend?

    b.   How much does the chicken pie cost?

11. Melody has 98 stickers. She gives $\frac{2}{7}$ of them to her sister and $\frac{3}{5}$ of the remainder to her brother. If she wants to increase her collection of stickers to twice what she had originally, how many more stickers must Melody buy?

12. Jacky bakes some biscuits. He keeps $\frac{3}{7}$ of the biscuits in container A, $\frac{5}{8}$ of the remainder in container B, and the rest in container C. There are 21 more biscuits in container A than in container C. How many biscuits does Jacky bake?

Lesson 4.3   Multiplying Improper Fractions by Fractions

Find the products.

1. $\dfrac{3}{8} \times \dfrac{5}{2}$

2. $\dfrac{1}{2} \times \dfrac{7}{3}$

3. $\dfrac{4}{5} \times \dfrac{5}{4}$

4. $\dfrac{5}{3} \times \dfrac{9}{4}$

5. $\dfrac{14}{9} \times \dfrac{15}{7}$

6. $\dfrac{16}{15} \times \dfrac{25}{2}$

Multiply. Express each product in simplest form.

7. $\dfrac{7}{4} \times \dfrac{9}{14}$

8. $\dfrac{8}{5} \times \dfrac{3}{4}$

9. $\dfrac{14}{9} \times \dfrac{6}{7}$

10. $\dfrac{9}{7} \times \dfrac{5}{6}$

11. $\dfrac{9}{8} \times \dfrac{4}{7}$

12. $\dfrac{7}{5} \times \dfrac{9}{14}$

13. $\dfrac{9}{5} \times \dfrac{10}{3}$

14. $\dfrac{17}{12} \times \dfrac{9}{4}$

15. $\dfrac{7}{3} \times \dfrac{12}{5}$

16. $\dfrac{14}{6} \times \dfrac{8}{7}$

17. $\dfrac{10}{7} \times \dfrac{14}{9}$

18. $\dfrac{13}{10} \times \dfrac{15}{8}$

Lesson 4.4 Multiplying Mixed Numbers and Whole Numbers

Multiply. Express each product in simplest form.

1. $3\frac{4}{5} \times 2$

2. $2\frac{3}{4} \times 8$

3. $2\frac{1}{6} \times 4$

4. $21 \times 1\frac{6}{7}$

5. $40 \times 2\frac{5}{8}$

6. $6 \times 3\frac{4}{9}$

7. $3\frac{2}{3} \times 17$ **8.** $2\frac{3}{7} \times 16$

9. $2\frac{5}{9} \times 12$ **10.** $18 \times 1\frac{7}{8}$

11. $14 \times 3\frac{3}{10}$ **12.** $9 \times 2\frac{5}{6}$

Name: _____   **Date:** _____

Complete.

13. There are 15 muffins.

Circle the 15 muffins into 3 equal groups.

$\frac{2}{3}$ of 15 = _____

14. What is $\frac{3}{5}$ of 40?

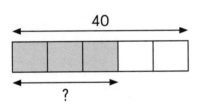

5 units = _____

1 unit = _____

3 units = _____

So, $\frac{3}{5}$ of 40 = _____

15.   What is $\frac{4}{7} \times 49$?

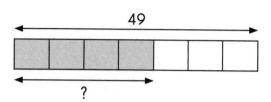

7 units = _____

1 unit = _____

4 units = _____

$\frac{4}{7} \times 49$ = _____

16.   What is $\frac{5}{8}$ of 64?

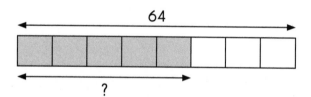

Solve.

17. $\frac{5}{6} \times 60$

18. $\frac{3}{7} \times 56$

19. $\frac{7}{8} \times 48$

20. $\frac{2}{9} \times 72$

21. $\frac{3}{10} \times 100$

22. $\frac{7}{12} \times 96$

23. Charlene has 32 hairpins. She gives $\frac{3}{8}$ of the hairpins to her sister. How many hairpins does Charlene give to her sister?

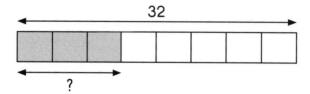

Lesson 4.5   Real-World Problems: Multiplying with Mixed Numbers

Solve. Show your work.

1. The Smith family drinks $1\frac{4}{5}$ gallons of apple juice each day. The apple juice is packed in 2 gallon cartons. How many cartons does Mrs. Smith need to buy every week?

2. Lily uses $1\frac{3}{4}$ yards of ribbon to make a knot. She wants to make 9 similar knots for her cousins. How many yards of ribbon does Lily need? Round your answer to the nearest yard.

3.   Puppy A is $\frac{3}{4}$ as heavy as puppy B. Puppy C is twice as heavy as puppy A. If the weight of puppy B is 8 pounds, find the weight of puppy C.

4.   A flowerbed is $3\frac{3}{4}$ meters long and 2 meters wide. Uncle James wants to build a border around the flowerbed. The width of the border is $\frac{1}{2}$ meter. The cost of building the border is \$20 per square meter. How much does Uncle James have to pay to have the border built?

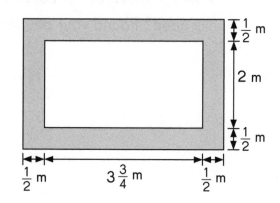

Lesson 4.6   Dividing Fractions and Whole Numbers

Shade parts of the model to show the division expression.
Then fill in the blanks.

1. $\frac{2}{3} \div 4$

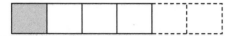

 is shaded.

$\frac{2}{3} \div 4 =$ _____

Divide. Draw a model to help you.

2. $\frac{1}{6} \div 2$

Divide. Draw a model to help you.

3. $\frac{8}{9} \div 8$

Divide. Express each answer in simplest form.

4. $\frac{4}{5} \div 6$

5. $\frac{7}{8} \div 21$

6. $\frac{9}{10} \div 3$

7. $\frac{5}{6} \div 15$

Solve. Show your work.

8. How many one quarters ($\frac{1}{4}$) are there in 3 wholes?

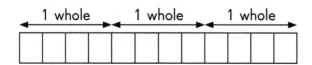

9. How many one-thirds ($\frac{1}{3}$) are there in 4 wholes?

Divide.

10. $4 \div \frac{1}{2}$ **11.** $6 \div \frac{1}{4}$

12. $5 \div \frac{1}{3}$ **13.** $2 \div \frac{1}{5}$

14. $2 \div \frac{1}{6}$ **15.** $3 \div \frac{1}{8}$

16. $3 \div \frac{1}{7}$ **17.** $4 \div \frac{1}{9}$

Solve. Show your work.

18.   A bottle contains $\frac{5}{12}$ gallon of paint. Mr. Jacobs pours all the paint equally into 5 pots. How much paint is there in each pot?

19.   During lunch, $\frac{1}{2}$ of a loaf of bread is shared equally among 5 girls. What fraction of the loaf of bread does each girl have?

20. A string of length $\frac{9}{10}$ yard is cut into 6 equal pieces. What is the total length of 2 of the pieces?

21.   Peggy had a bag of nuts. She ate $\frac{1}{5}$ of the nuts and gave the remaining nuts to 3 friends equally. What fraction of the nuts did each friend get?

22. Aunt Amy had 1 liter of milk. She gave the milk to her four children. Jane, the youngest child, divided her milk equally to her 5 kittens.

a. How did Jane work out the amount of milk for each kitten? Show your answer in liters.

b. How many milliliters of milk did each kitten get?

Test Prep

$\boxed{\diagup 50}$

for Chapters 1 to 4

Multiple Choice   (10 × 2 points = 20 points)

Fill in the circle next to the correct answer.

1.   425,760 = $\boxed{}$ + 5,000 + 60

What is the missing number?

(A) 427   (B) 42,070   (C) 420,700   (D) 427,000

2.   In 2,591,380, the value of the digit 9 is $\boxed{}$ times the value of the digit 3.
What is the missing number?

(A) 3   (B) 30   (C) 300   (D) 3,000

3.   Which of these numbers has a digit 2 with a value of 20,000?

(A) 28,451   (B) 452,763   (C) 295,410   (D) 214,600

4.   Which is the expanded form of 28,409?

(A) 28,000 + 400 + 9

(B) 20,000 + 8,400 + 9

(C) 20,000 + 8,000 + 400 + 9

(D) 20,000 + 8,000 + 409

5. What comes next in the number pattern?

2,500   3,000   4,000   5,500   7,500   ☐

(A) 8,500   (B) 9,000   (C) 9,500   (D) 10,000

6. What is the best estimate for the value of 38,950 ÷ 230?

(A) 100   (B) 200   (C) 300   (D) 400

7. What is the estimated product of 798 and 37?

(A) 21,000   (B) 24,000   (C) 28,000   (D) 32,000

8. Wayne puts 3,930 paper clips equally into 19 packets. How many paper clips are left?

(A) 14   (B) 16   (C) 206   (D) 260

9. What is the value of $3\frac{1}{6} - 1\frac{5}{8}$?

(A) $1\frac{13}{24}$ (B) $2\frac{13}{24}$ (C) $2\frac{11}{24}$ (D) $4\frac{19}{24}$

10. What is the product of $\frac{5}{8}$ and $\frac{2}{10}$ in simplest form?

(A) $\frac{10}{80}$ (B) $\frac{7}{18}$ (C) $\frac{1}{8}$ (D) $\frac{33}{40}$

Short Answer (10 × 2 points = 20 points)

Write your answers in the space given.

11. Write the standard form of two million, four hundred sixty-seven thousand, fifty-eight.

Answer: _____

12. What is the difference between the values of the digits 8 and 9 in the number 1,890,600?

Answer: _____

13. Use all the digits shown to form the least possible 6-digit odd number. The first digit should not be a zero.

2   3   0   5   8   4

Answer: _____

14. Arrange the numbers in order from greatest to least.

319,500   290,500   2,090,500   3,190,500   3,090,500

Answer: _____

15.   Find the value of $301 \div 7 - 36 \times 3 \div 4$.

Answer: _____

16.   Find the value of $318 \div (34 - 28) \times 8$.

Answer: _____

17.   Find the value of $2\frac{3}{4} + 1\frac{5}{6}$.

Answer: _____

18.   During a sale, 36 similar handbags are sold for a total of $1,620. Before the sale, the same number of handbags were sold at $49 each. What is the difference between the amount of money made before and after the sale?

Answer: $_____

19.   John mixes $3\frac{5}{8}$ gallons of blue paint with $2\frac{3}{10}$ gallons of yellow paint. How many gallons of mixed paint does he get? Express your answer as a decimal.

Answer: _____ gallons

20. Mr. Muller had $\frac{7}{8}$ pound of meat. He used $\frac{2}{5}$ of it to make burgers. How much meat did Mr. Muller have left?

Answer: _____ pound

Extended Response (Questions 21 and 22: 2 × 3 points, Question 23: 4 points)

Solve. Show your work.

21. Mrs. Jones and Mr. Graham had the same amount of money at first. After Mrs. Jones bought a computer that cost $2,055, she had $\frac{1}{4}$ as much money as Mr. Graham. How much money did Mr. Graham have?

22. Colin and Rosie had the same number of cashews at first. Each day, Colin ate 5 cashews and Rosie ate 8 cashews. When Rosie had 4 cashews left, Colin had 10 times as many cashews left as Rosie. How many cashews did each child have at first?

23. Mr. Garcia pays $834 for some model cars and model planes. Each model car costs $52 and each model plane costs $14 less than each model car. Mr. Garcia buys 3 more model planes than cars. How many model planes does he buy?

Name: _____ **Date:** _____

Algebra

Lesson 5.1   Number Patterns and Relationships

Find the next three terms of each number pattern.

1.   1,   5,   25,   _____,   _____,   _____

2.   1,   8,   27,   64,   125,   _____,   _____,   _____

3.   2,   6,   12,   20,   _____,   _____,   _____

4.   1,   5,   3,   15,   13,   _____,   _____,   _____

5.   1,   1,   2,   3,   5,   8,   _____,   _____,   _____

Complete the table and answer the questions that follow.

Length of Side of Square (in.)	1	2	3	4	5	6
Area of Square (in.²)	1	4	9			

6.   What is the area of a square with a side of
   a.   9 inches?

   b.   12 inches?

7.   What is the length of a square of area
   a.   64 square inches?

b. 100 square inches?

Complete the table and answer the questions that follow.

Number of Bags	1	2	3	4	5
Cost of Each ($)	2.50				

8. What is the cost of
   a. 7 bags?

   b. 10 bags?

9.   How many bags cost
      a. $20?

      b. $37.50?

Lesson 5.2   Using Letters as Numbers

Write an expression for each situation.

1.   Add 8 to w

2.   Subtract 10 from a

3.   Sum of p and $\frac{3}{4}$

4.   Subtract $6y$ from 5

5.   Multiply 6 by g

6.   Divide $3k$ by 2

7.   4 times as many as h

8.   12 less than $5s$

9.   8 more than $7b$

10.   Divide $5d$ by 4

Evaluate each expression for *m* = 4.

11. $11 - m$

12. $m + 9$

Evaluate each expression for *k* = 8.

13. $3k + 7$

14. $12 + 6k$

15. $30 - 2k$

16. $7k - 19$

Evaluate each expression for $y = 6$.

17. $\dfrac{y + 8}{2}$

18. $\dfrac{y + 9}{3}$

19. $\dfrac{5y + 20}{5}$

20. $\dfrac{8y}{3} - 7$

Write an expression for each situation.

21. Each box of crayons costs x dollars. How much does Mrs. Smith pay for 5 boxes of crayons?

22. Alyssa has 6*p* dollars. Her brother has 15 dollars. How much more money does Alyssa have than her brother?

23. Mrs. Estrada has 5*m* liters of milk. Her family drinks 2 liters each day. How much milk is left after a week?

24. Gary has 3y comics. Shaun has 8 comics. They share their comics equally. How many comics does each of them have?

25. Evan bought k bottles of pasta sauce at $4 each. He gave $10 to the cashier. How much change did he receive?

26. At a bookstore, 8 similar books cost *y* dollars. What is the cost of 3 such books?

27. John has *y* stickers. He keeps 20 stickers for himself and gives the remainder to his two sisters equally. How many stickers does each sister get?

28. Kenny has *m* guppies and 10 angelfish. He buys another 20 guppies and 30 angelfish. How many fish does Kenny have now?

29. A string of length *g* inches is cut into two pieces. One piece is 10 inches longer than the other. Find the length of the shorter piece.

Lesson 5.3 Simplifying Algebraic Expressions

Simplify each expression.

1. $g + g + g$

2. $4w + 6w$

3. $8a - 3a$

4. $15b - 7b$

5. $16h - 7h - 2h$

6. $20k - 6k - 8k$

7. $9d - 5d + 7d$

8. $17n + 6n - 8n$

Simplify each expression.

9. $5x + 7x - 4$

10. $6 + 7g + 3g$

11. $8n + 5 - 4n$

12. $8d - 5 + 7d - 9d$

13. $3 + 8k + 9 - 5k$

14. $10w + 11 - 3w - 8$

15. $10 + 5h - 6 + 8h$

16. $11 + 7m - 6 - 4m$

17. $8 + 12s - 7 - 9s + 4$

18. $5n + 10 + 8n - 9n + 3$

Lesson 5.4   Inequalities and Equations

Complete with >, <, or =.

1.   For $k = 4$, $3k$ ◯ 15.

2.   For $k = 5$, $7k$ ◯ 35.

3.   For $k = 6$, $6k$ ◯ 30.

4.   For $k = 10$, $8k$ ◯ 50.

Complete with >, <, or = for w = 7.

5. $2w - 5$ ◯ 6

6. $4w + 3$ ◯ 36

7. $5w - 8$ ◯ 20

8. $20 - 2w$ ◯ 6

Solve each equation.

9. $4n = 28$

10. $3d + 5 = 17$

11. $10w - 18 = 42$

12. $42 + 6h = 84$

13. $7m - 35 = 5 + 2m$

14. $4k + 44 = 10k - 10$

Lesson 5.5   Real-World Problems: Algebra

Solve. Show your work.

1.   Joan is y years old. Her father is 4 times as old as she is and 28 years older than her brother.

    a.   Find, in terms of y, the age of Joan's brother.

    b.   If $y = 12$, how old is her brother?

2.   Mr. Tyler wants to rent a car for n days. The car rental company charges a fixed fee of $120 and an extra $18 for each day of rental.

    a.   Find, in terms of n, the cost of renting the car.

    b.   If $n = 8$, find the cost of renting the car.

3.   Kenneth has $5. He spends g cents every day. How much money does he have left after one week?

   a.   Express your answer in cents.

   b.   Express your answer in dollars.

4.   The total age of Amelia, Bernard, and Cindy is $10w$ years. Amelia is $2w$ years old. Bernard is as old as Cindy.

   a.   Express Cindy's age in terms of w.

   b.   If $w = 4$, how old is Cindy?

5.   Patrick buys 3 model A planes for p dollars each and Amanda buys
2 model B planes for $36.

   a.   How much does Patrick pay for the model A planes?

   b.   Find the value of p so that Patrick and Amanda pay the same
amount of money for the planes they bought.

6.   Nancy has $(4k + 6)$ meters of ribbon. Kevin has $(6k - 2)$ meters
of ribbon.

   a.   If $k = 5$, who has the shorter ribbon?

   b.   For what value of k will they have the same length of ribbon?

7. Mr. Anderson earns $50b$ dollars a month. Each month he spends $28b$ dollars and saves the rest. Does he save more than he spends?

8. Anne has p game cards. Benny has 3 times as many game cards as Anne. Colin has 30 game cards. What is the least value of p so that Anne and Benny together have more game cards than Colin?

Put on Your Thinking Cap!

Solve. Show your work.

1. A box of crackers has a mass of p kilograms. When empty, the box has a mass of 200 grams. What is the total mass of the crackers in 5 such boxes? Express your answer in kilograms.

2. A printing company charges a fixed fee of $30 for printing wedding cards and an extra $2 for printing each card. Mr. Johnson wants to print x wedding cards.
   a. How much money will Mr. Johnson pay in terms of x?

   b. If Mr. Johnson wants to print 200 cards, how much will he have to pay?

3. Lena has 80 stickers. She gives 5*m* stickers to her friends and shares the remaining stickers equally with her 2 brothers.
    a. How many stickers does she give each brother in terms of *m*?

    b. If *m* = 4, how many stickers does each brother get?

4. Tom's monthly allowance is *k* dollars. Jerry's monthly allowance is 3 times as much as Tom's monthly allowance. Danny's monthly allowance is $20 more than Jerry's monthly allowance.
    a. What is their total monthly allowance in terms of *k*?

    b. If Tom's monthly allowance is $18, find their total monthly allowance.

Area

Lesson 6.1   Finding the Area of a Rectangle with Fractional Side Lengths

Find the area of each rectangle.

1.   The length of a rectangle is $\frac{4}{5}$ foot and its width is $\frac{3}{8}$ foot. Find the area of the rectangle.

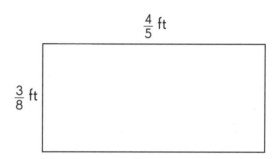

2.   The length of a rectangle is $\frac{20}{9}$ inches and its width is $\frac{3}{5}$ inch. Find the area of the rectangle.

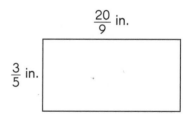

3.   The length of a rectangle is $10\frac{1}{2}$ centimeters and its width is

6 centimeters. Find the area of the rectangle.

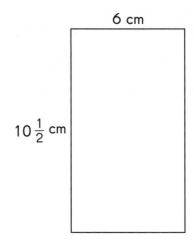

6 cm

$10\frac{1}{2}$ cm

4.   The length of a rectangular field is $20\frac{4}{5}$ meters and its width is

15 meters. Find the area of the field.

Lesson 6.2 Base and Height of a Triangle

Name the height for each given base.

In triangle *ABC*,

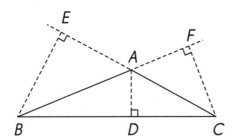

1. if the base is $\overline{BC}$, the height is _____.

2. if the base is $\overline{AC}$, the height is _____.

3. if the base is $\overline{AB}$, the height is _____.

Name the base for each given height.

In triangle *PQR*,

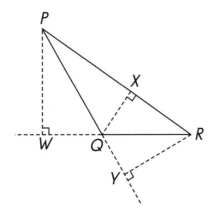

4. if the height is $\overline{PW}$, the base is _____.

5. if the height is $\overline{QX}$, the base is _____.

6. if the height is $\overline{RY}$, the base is _____.

For each triangle, use a drawing triangle to draw the height for the given base.

7.

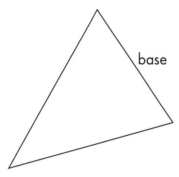

8.

9.

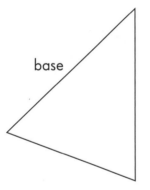

10.

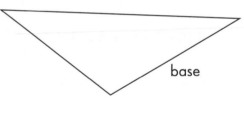

Name the base and height of triangle _KLM_.

11.

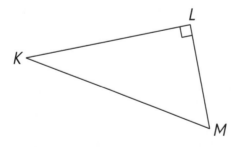

Base = _____

Height = _____

12.

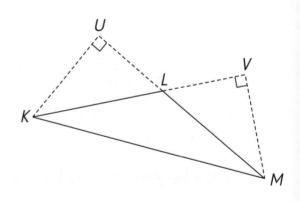

Base = _____

Height = _____

Lesson 6.3   Finding the Area of a Triangle

Find the area of each shaded triangle.

1.

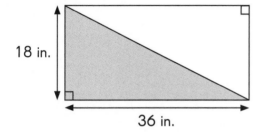

18 in.

36 in.

2.

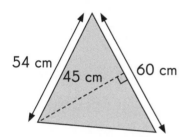

54 cm

45 cm

60 cm

3.

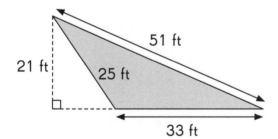

21 ft

25 ft

51 ft

33 ft

4.

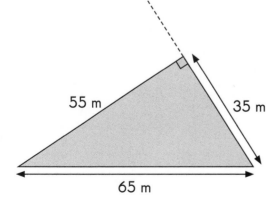

55 m

35 m

65 m

Find the area of each shaded triangle.

5.

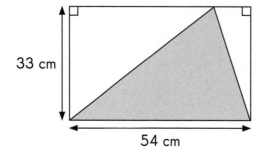

6.

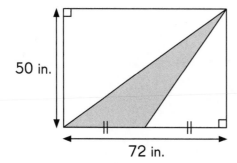

7.

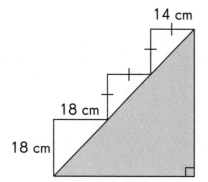

8.

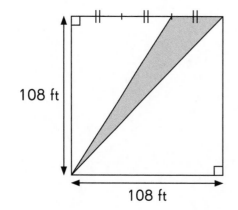

Put on Your Thinking Cap!

Solve. Show your work.

1. In the figure, $BD = DE$. Find the shaded area.

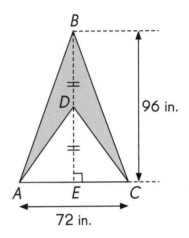

96 in.

72 in.

2. $ABCD$ is a square of side 60 centimeters. Find the shaded area.

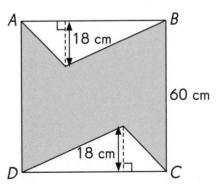

18 cm

60 cm

18 cm

3. Sharon has a piece of rectangular construction paper 60 cm by 30 cm. She cuts out five identical triangles. The height of each triangle is half the width of the paper. Find the area of the remaining piece of paper.

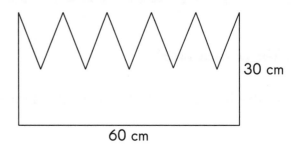

30 cm

60 cm

4. In rectangle $ABCD$, $\overline{EF}$ is perpendicular to $\overline{BD}$. Find the shaded area.

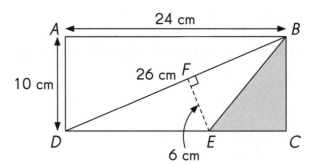

5.   Find the shaded area.

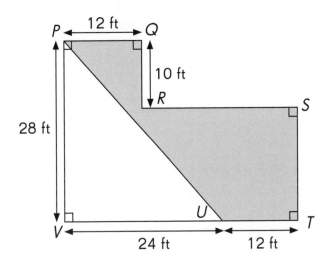

6.   In triangle *ABC*, the length of $\overline{CD}$ is twice the length of $\overline{EF}$.
The length of $\overline{AG}$ is $\frac{1}{3}$ the length of $\overline{AB}$. Find the shaded area.

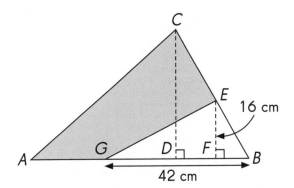

7. In the figure, the length of the side of the smaller square is
12 centimeters and the length of the side of the bigger square is
15 centimeters. Find the shaded area.

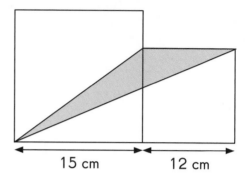

15 cm   12 cm

8. The figure shows two identical triangles overlapping each other.
The overlapped area is a square. Find the unshaded area.

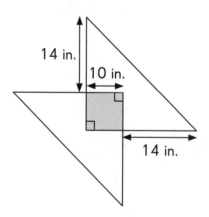

14 in.

10 in.

14 in.

Ratio

Lesson 7.1   Finding Ratio

Solve.

A packet of breakfast cereal contains these ingredients:

Dried fruit	16 grams
Walnuts	23 grams
Rolled oats	11 grams
Cornflakes	10 grams

1.   Find the total mass of the ingredients in the packet of breakfast cereal.

2.   Complete the table to show the ratios.

The Ratio of	Ratio
The mass of walnuts to the mass of cornflakes	
The mass of rolled oats to the total mass of cereal	
The total mass of cereal to the mass of walnuts	
The total mass of dried fruit and walnuts to the mass of cornflakes	
The total mass of cereal to the mass of cornflakes	

Solve.

3. A concrete mixture is made up of 3 parts water, 4 parts cement, and 5 parts sand. Find the ratios of:

   a. the amount of cement to the amount of water

   b. the amount of sand to the amount of the concrete mixture

4. There are 20 animals in a pond. Of these animals, 7 are frogs, 8 are fish, and the rest are tortoises. Find the ratios of:

   a. the number of frogs to the total number of animals

   b. the number of fish to the number of tortoises

5. Malik had $56 at first. He had $27 left after giving some money to both Anne and John. If John received $15, what was the ratio of the amount of money Anne received to the amount of money John received?

Lesson 7.2   Equivalent Ratios

Find the missing number in each set of equivalent ratios.

1. $3 : 7 =$ _____ $: 28$

2. $4 : 9 = 24 :$ _____

3. $8 : 5 =$ _____ $: 35$

4. $2 : 7 = 12 :$ _____

5. $5 : 6 = 60 :$ _____

6. $28 : 49 = 4 :$ _____

7. $81 : 27 =$ _____ $: 3$

8. $72 : 48 = 12 :$ _____

Name: _____   **Date:** _____

Write each ratio in simplest form.

9.   14 : 21 = _____

10.   45 : 18 = _____

11.   56 : 32 = _____

12.   27 : 45 = _____

13.   64 : 40 = _____

14.   66 : 78 = _____

15.   42 : 63 = _____

16.   48 : 12 = _____

Lesson 7.3   Real-World Problems: Ratios

Solve. Show your work.

1.   A worker uses 4 gray tiles for every 5 blue tiles that he uses.
   a.   If he uses 60 gray tiles, how many blue tiles does he use?

   b.   If he uses 540 tiles altogether, how many gray tiles does he use?

2.   At a certain time of day, a pole, 5 meters tall, casts a 3-meter shadow.
   a.   The shadow of a building beside the pole is 18 meters long.
       How tall is the building?

   b.   How long will the shadow of a 45-meter building be?

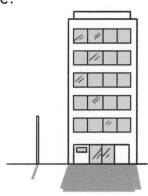

3. There were 18 boys and 16 girls on a school bus. At a bus stop, 4 girls got off the bus and 3 boys got on the bus. What is the ratio of the number of boys to the number of girls on the bus now?

4. The ratio of the length of a rectangle to its width is 5 : 3. The width is 16 inches shorter than the length. Find the area of the rectangle.

Lesson 7.4   Ratios in Fraction Form

Solve.

Rayza baked 20 chicken pies. Michelle baked 12 more chicken pies than Rayza.

1. What is the ratio of the number of chicken pies Michelle baked to the number of chicken pies Rayza baked?

2. Express the number of chicken pies Michelle baked as a fraction of the number of chicken pies Rayza baked.

3. What fraction of the number of chicken pies baked by Michelle was the number of chicken pies baked by Rayza?

4. What fraction of the total number of chicken pies baked by both girls was the number of chicken pies baked by Michelle?

5. How many times the number of chicken pies baked by Rayza was the number of chicken pies baked by Michelle?

Solve.

The number of tropical fish Leon has is $\frac{3}{8}$ of the number of tropical fish Haru has.

6.   Find the ratio of the number of tropical fish Leon has to the number of tropical fish Haru has.

7.   What fraction of the number of tropical fish Haru has is the number of tropical fish Leon has?

8.   How many times the number of tropical fish Leon has is the number of tropical fish Haru has?

9.   If Leon has 35 fewer tropical fish than Haru, how many fish do they have altogether?

Lesson 7.5   Comparing Three Quantities

Find the missing numbers in each set of equivalent ratios.

1. $2 : 7 : 4 = 10 :$ _____ : _____

2. $3 : 8 : 6 =$ _____ $: 24 :$ _____

3. $7 : 9 : 12 =$ _____ $:$ _____ $: 48$

4. $5 : 8 : 9 =$ _____ $: 56 :$ _____

Write each ratio in simplest form.

5. 12 : 8 : 20 = _____ : _____ : _____

6. 36 : 18 : 30 = _____ : _____ : _____

7. 27 : 45 : 72 = _____ : _____ : _____

8. 32 : 56 : 64 = _____ : _____ : _____

Mid-Year Test

Multiple Choice (20 × 2 points = 40 points)

Fill in the circle next to the correct answer.

1. In 784,732, the value of the digit 7 in the hundred thousands place is ☐ times the value of 7 in the hundreds place.
What is the missing number?

Ⓐ 100   Ⓑ 1,000   Ⓒ 10,000   Ⓓ 100,000

2. What is the value of 48 ÷ 8 × 2 + (30 − 16) × 7?

Ⓐ 40   Ⓑ 101   Ⓒ 110   Ⓓ 171

3. ☐ ÷ 29 = 17 × 11

What is the missing number?

Ⓐ 187   Ⓑ 4,957   Ⓒ 5,423   Ⓓ 5,742

4. What is the sum of all the numbers in the box that are multiples of 7?

| 56 | 36 | 72 | 84 |
| 63 | 98 | 24 | 48 |

Ⓐ 119   Ⓑ 203   Ⓒ 217   Ⓓ 301

5.   I am a number. If you multiply me by 3 and subtract 84 from the product, I will become 18. What number am I?

(A) 34   (B) 36   (C) 304   (D) 306

6.   How many thousands are there in the product of 53 hundreds and 60 tens?

(A) 31   (B) 318   (C) 3,180   (D) 31,800

7.   The sum of two numbers is 760 and their difference is 200. Find the greater number.

(A) 280   (B) 480   (C) 560   (D) 960

8.   Mr. Kellman is twice as old as his son who is 26 years old. What will be their total age in 7 years?

(A) 71 years   (B) 78 years   (C) 85 years   (D) 92 years

9.   Ivy has $3p$ grapes. She keeps 10 grapes for herself and gives the remainder to two brothers equally. How many grapes does each brother get?

(A) $3p - 10$ (B) $\dfrac{3p}{2}$ (C) $\dfrac{3p}{2}\ 10$ (D) $\dfrac{3p - 10}{3}$

10. The container shown has a capacity of 60 milliliters.
What fraction of it is empty?

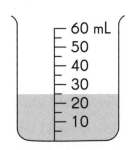

(A) $\frac{5}{12}$ (B) $\frac{1}{3}$ (C) $\frac{7}{12}$ (D) $\frac{5}{6}$

11. What is the area of the whole figure?

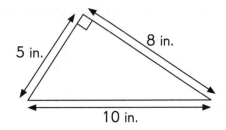

5 in.

8 in.

10 in.

(A) 20 in.^{2} (B) 25 in.^{2} (C) 40 in.^{2} (D) 50 in.^{2}

12. Find the shaded area of the square if $AB = BC = CD$.

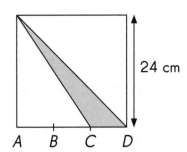

24 cm

A B C D

(A) 72 cm^2 (B) 96 cm^2 (C) 192 cm^2 (D) 288 cm^2

13.   Evaluate $2 \times 30 - [28 + (100 - 36) \div 4]$.

    Ⓐ 16　　　　　Ⓑ 24　　　　　Ⓒ 48　　　　　Ⓓ 49

14.   A stick is $\frac{3}{4}$ yard long. A rope is $\frac{1}{2}$ yard long. A plank is $\frac{5}{8}$ yard long. What is the difference in length between the longest and the shortest length of these three items?

    Ⓐ $\frac{3}{4}$ yd　　　Ⓑ $\frac{3}{8}$ yd　　　Ⓒ $\frac{1}{2}$ yd　　　Ⓓ $\frac{1}{4}$ yd

15.   There are 84 squash balls and 36 tennis balls in a basket. What is the ratio of the number of tennis balls to the number of squash balls?

    Ⓐ 3 : 7　　　　Ⓑ 7 : 3　　　　Ⓒ 7 : 10　　　　Ⓓ 10 : 3

16.   Maria spent $\frac{1}{5}$ of her savings on a storybook. She spent $\frac{3}{8}$ of the remaining amount on a comic book. What fraction of her savings was spent on the comic book?

    Ⓐ $\frac{17}{40}$　　　　Ⓑ $\frac{4}{5}$　　　　Ⓒ $\frac{1}{2}$　　　　Ⓓ $\frac{3}{10}$

17.   Pearl discovers that $\frac{2}{5}$ of her savings is equal to $\frac{1}{2}$ of her sister's savings. If Pearl has $20 more than her sister, how much savings does her sister have?

    Ⓐ $40　　　　Ⓑ $60　　　　Ⓒ $80　　　　Ⓓ $100

18. The length of a rectangle is $12\frac{3}{4}$ inches and its width is 8 inches.
Find the area of the rectangle.

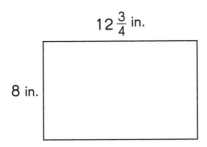

$12\frac{3}{4}$ in.

8 in.

(A) 96 in.²   (B) 98 in.²   (C) 106 in.²   (D) 102 in.²

19. Pearl discovers that $\frac{2}{5}$ of her savings is equal to $\frac{1}{2}$ of her sister's savings.
Find the ratio of Pearl's savings to her sister's savings.

(A) 2 : 1   (B) 1 : 2   (C) 4 : 5   (D) 5 : 4

20. Sophia wanted to knit a scarf $1\frac{2}{5}$ meters long. On Monday, she knit
$\frac{1}{4}$ of the length. On Tuesday, she knit another 45 centimeters.
What fraction of the scarf did she knit altogether?

(A) $\frac{3}{7}$ (B) $\frac{4}{7}$ (C) $\frac{7}{20}$ (D) $\frac{9}{28}$

Short Answer   (20 × 2 points = 40 points)

Write your answers in the space given.

21. What is the difference in value between the digit 9 and the digit 7
in the number 983,752?

Answer: _____

22. What is the product of 150 and 37, rounded to the nearest thousand?

Answer: _____

23.   Find the value of $96 \div (7 + 5) + 19 \times 4$.

Answer: _____

24.   Find the value of $\dfrac{3x}{2} - 7$ if $x = 8$.

Answer: _____

25.   Jessica and Olivia shared $255. Jessica received $\dfrac{5}{12}$ as much money as Olivia. How much money did Olivia receive?

Answer: $_____

26.   There are $\dfrac{3}{7}$ as many girls as there are boys in a field. There are 64 more boys than girls. How many children are in the field?

Answer: _____

27.   What is the area of the shaded triangle *ABC*?

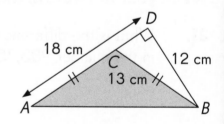

Answer: _____ square centimeters

28.   What fraction of the square *ABCD* is unshaded?

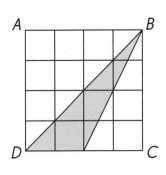

Answer: _____

29.   The figure is made up of a triangle and a rectangle. It has a total area of 160 square inches. *AB* = *BC* = *BF* = *FE*. Find the length of $\overline{AB}$.

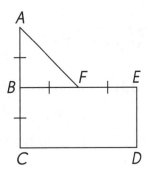

Answer: _____ inches

30.   *ABCD* is a rectangle. What fraction of the rectangle is shaded?

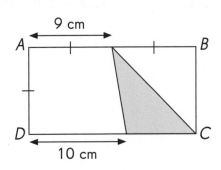

Answer: _____

31.   There are 96 members in a sports club. The ratio of the number of male members to the number of female members is 5 : 3. If 4 more female members join the club, what is the new ratio of the number of male members to the number of female members?

Answer: _____

32.   There are 32 students in a class. Of these students, $\frac{5}{8}$ are boys. If 5 girls wear glasses, how many girls do not wear glasses?

Answer: _____

33.   John has 78 storybooks. He donates $\frac{2}{3}$ of the books to a school and gives $\frac{1}{2}$ of the remainder to his sister. How many books does John give to his sister?

Answer: _____

34. $BC = CD = DE$. What is the area of triangle ACD?

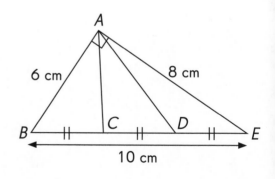

Answer: _____ square centimeters

35. Rainer had $133 and Joel had $57. After they each bought a T-shirt, Rainer had 3 times as much money left as Joel. The prices of the T-shirts were the same. How much did each T-shirt cost?

Answer: $_____

36. Sam buys a game console and a cartridge for $546. The cartridge costs $\frac{1}{5}$ as much as the game console. Find the cost of the game console.

Answer: $_____

37. Mike has 288 stickers. If he gives 18 stickers to Ken, both of them have the same number of stickers. How many stickers do they have in all?

Answer: _____

38. There are red, blue, and white buttons in a box. 300 of them are white buttons. There are half as many red buttons as white buttons. The number of blue buttons is three times the number of red buttons. How many buttons are in the box?

Answer: _____

39. The capacity of a water tank is 500 liters. After a downpour, $\frac{3}{5}$ of the tank is full. Then, $\frac{5}{8}$ of the water in the tank is piped to a water distillation plant. How much water is left in the tank? Express your answer as a decimal.

Answer: _____ liters

40. Mr. Johnson drives a distance of $(6y + 5)$ miles. Miss Tucker drives a distance of $(8y - 7)$ miles. If $y = 5$, who drives farther? How much farther?

Answer: _____

Extended Response   (5 × 4 points = 20 points)

Solve. Show your work.

41. A bag is made with 1,350 green, blue, and white beads. Twice as many green beads as blue beads are used. The number of white beads is half of the total number of green and blue beads. How many green beads are used?

42.   The figure is made up of two squares. Find the shaded area.

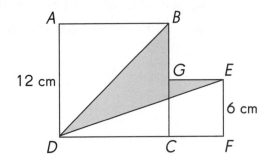

43.   Mary's mother made 102 chicken sandwiches and tuna sandwiches for Mary's birthday party. After her friends had eaten $\frac{5}{8}$ of the chicken sandwiches and $\frac{2}{3}$ of the tuna sandwiches, an equal number of chicken and tuna sandwiches were left. How many sandwiches of each type did Mary's mother make?

44. In a storeroom, there are 30 blue balls, 48 green balls, some red balls, and some white balls. There are 3 times as many green balls as red balls and 5 times as many blue balls as white balls.

  a. How many balls are there altogether?

  b. How many balls will be left in the room if $\frac{7}{10}$ of the balls are taken away?

45. The three brothers, Pete, Ben and Leon, have saved some money. Leon has twice as much as Pete. Ben has $\frac{3}{4}$ as much money as Pete. Leon has $135 more than Ben. How much money have they saved altogether?

Answers

Chapter 1

Lesson 1.1

1.

Hundred Thousands	Ten Thousands	Thousands	Hundreds	Tens	Ones
●● ●	●●● ●●	●●● ●●●	●● ●●		●

   a. three hundred fifty-six thousand, four hundred one
   b. 356,401

2. 28,199
3. 90,038
4. 412,603
5. 800,005
6. 507,700
7. 600,600
8. Fifty thousand, six hundred eighty
9. Two hundred fifty-five thousand, four hundred thirty
10. One hundred ninety-nine thousand, three hundred three
11. Eight hundred seventy-two thousand, nine hundred
12. Three hundred five thousand, seventy-two
13. 304,678
14. 876,430
15. 304,687
16. 876,403
17. Answers vary.
   Samples: 306,748; 346,780; 387,406

18.

Millions	Hundred Thousands	Ten Thousands	Thousands	Hundreds	Tens	Ones
●● ●● ●●	●●		●● ●●	● ●●	●	● ●●

   a. six million, two hundred four thousand, three hundred thirteen
   b. 6,204,313

19. 9,270,050
20. 6,084,101
21. 7,006,899
22. 4,502,015
23. 5,050,602
24. 8,400,085
25. 3,000,703

26. Eight million, eight hundred eight thousand, four hundred twenty-nine
27. Three million, two thousand, five hundred sixty-six
28. Five million, nine hundred seventy thousand, one hundred three
29. Two million, fifty thousand, sixty
30. Four million, seven hundred thousand, nine hundred
31. 1,023,596
32. Answers vary.
   Samples: 3,629,501; 3,269,510; 3,029,561
33. Answers vary.
   Samples: 3,902,615; 3,260,519; 3,150,269
34. Answers vary.
   Samples: 6,903,512; 6,935,012; 9,052,136

Lesson 1.2

1.

900,000
20,000
5,000
0
30
8

2. ten thousands
3. 90,000
4. 90,000
5. ten thousands
6. hundreds
7. hundred thousands
8. 5,000
9. 500
10. 500,000
11. 8
12. ten thousands
13. hundred thousands
14. 60,000; ten thousands
15. 0; 0
16. 10,000
17. 700,000
18. 4,000
19. 204,891
20. 570,030
21. 306,010

22.

| 7,000,000 |
| 800,000 |
| 0 |
| 3,000 |
| 500 |
| 20 |
| 4 |

23. 6; 60,000
24. millions
25. 780
26. 728,000
27. 6,085,323
28. 2,700,508
29. 1,976,805
30. 581,249

Lesson 1.3

1. 123,087
2. 625,897
3. 4,314,356
4. 32,049
5. 785,900
6. 5,468,015
7. 197,500 283,500 1,795,000 2,385,000
   2,583,000
8. 895,390 8,476,900 8,593,800
   8,746,800 8,764,500
9. 5,298,053 5,296,000 2,890,670
   980,576 594,287
10. 3,900,100 3,003,500 2,900,800
    390,300 303,500
11. a. 1,000
    b. 1,000
    c. 1,000; 479,270
    d. 479,270
12. a. 20,000
    b. 20,000
    c. 20,000; 4,440,000
    d. 4,440,000
13. 1,005,600; 1,205,600; count on by 200,000
14. 935,800; 920,800; count back by 15,000
15. 5,391,200; 5,441,200; count on by 50,000
16. 1,158,600; 1,058,500; count back by
    100,100

Lesson 1.4

1. 4,000
2. 28,000
3. 725,000
4. 300,000
5. 15,000
6. 8,000
7. 12,000
8. 2,000
9. 56,000
10. 81,000
11. 900
12. 500
13. 900
14. 600
15. 2,832 rounds to 3,000.
    1,475 rounds to 1,000.
    3,000 + 1,000 = 4,000
    The estimated number of tourists was 4,000.
16. 4,342 ÷ 7 is about 4,200 ÷ 7 = 600.
    The estimated number of visitors on Monday
    was 600.
17. 4 × $1,000 = $4,000
    His estimated total sales was $4,000.
18. 4 × $1,500 = $6,000
    His estimated total sales was $6,000.
19. 4 × $1,499 = $5,996
    His actual total sales was $5,996. Answers vary;
    Exercise 17 is easier to calculate; Exercise 18 gives
    an estimate that is closer to the actual total sales.

Put on Your Thinking Cap!

Thinking skill: Identifying patterns and relationships
Strategy: Look for pattern

1. 200,000
2. 9,750
3. 1,800,000
4. 1,000
5. 27,000
6. Thinking skill: Comparing
   Strategy: Use guess and check
   Solution: Estimate the number. Then guess
           and check your answers.
   20 × 20 = 400, 30 × 30 = 900
   600 is between 400 and 900 so the two
   numbers are greater than 20 but less than 30.
   24 × 25 = 600
   The page numbers are 24 and 25.
7. Thinking skill: Comparing
   Strategy: Use guess and check
   Solution: 9,805,472

8. Thinking skill: Comparing

   Strategy: Use guess and check

   Solution: 394,825 or 394,865

Chapter 2

Lesson 2.1

1. 6,541
2. 8,594
3. 6,471
4. 7,624
5. 2,538
6. 3,185
7. 13,176
8. 92,136
9. 25,192
10. 27,782
11. 75,792
12. 1,020,600
13. 908
14. 793
15. 56
16. 84
17. 436
18. 3286.5
19. Answers vary.

   Samples: 679 × 11 × 91 = 679,679;
   189 × 11 × 91 = 189,189. The answer will
   be the 3-digit number repeated.

Lesson 2.2

1. 380
2. 7,460
3. 6,240
4. 8,570
5. 7,580
6. 6,800
7. 10
8. 190
9. 10
10. 10
11. 6,400
12. 80,800
13. 8; 448; 4,480
14. 4; 3,024; 30,240
15. 5; 3,400; 34,000
16. 857; 6; 5,142; 51,420
17. 1,520
18. 45,760
19. 14,700
20. 26,250
21. 4,700
22. 32,500
23. 16,800
24. 231,000
25. 192,000
26. 759,000
27. 100
28. 7,120
29. 1,000
30. 100
31. 7,910
32. 5,200
33. 6; 144; 14,400
34. 4; 432; 43,200
35. 5; 800; 80,000
36. 3; 111; 111,000
37. 8; 824; 824,000
38. 4; 1,300; 1,300,000

39. 146,300
40. 1,314,000

Lesson 2.3

1. 950; 950 × 10 = 9,500;
   9,500 × 10 = 95,000
2. 860; 860 × 10 = 8,600;
   8,600 × 10 = 86,000
3. 4,530; 4,530 × 10 = 45,300;
   45,300 × 10 = 453,000
4. 1,280; 1,280 × 10 = 12,800;
   12,800 × 10 = 128,000
5. 62,500; 62,500 × 10 = 625,000;
   625,000 × 10 = 6,250,000
6. 93,600; 93,600 × 10 = 936,000;
   936,000 × 10 = 9,360,000
7. 744; 7,440
8. 1,735; 17,350
9. 548; 54,800
10. 4,512; 451,200
11. 3,156; 3,156,000
12. 1,764; 1,764,000

Lesson 2.4

1. 3,680
2. 4,770
3. 2,254
4. 3,016
5. 2,331
6. 3,055
7. 3,698
8. 8,064
9. 30,520
10. 22,200
11. 13,365
12. 47,936
13. 49,452
14. 97,278
15. 93,834
16. 74,592

Lesson 2.5

1. 720
2. 280
3. 2,300
4. 68,000
5. 232
6. 1,600
7. 10
8. 10
9. 3,980
10. 55,000
11. 10; 930; 310
12. 5; 950; 5; 190
13. 6; 12,600; 6; 2,100
14. 1,500
15. 6,200
16. 5,400
17. 3,820
18. 48
19. 357
20. 79
21. 350
22. 192
23. 275,000
24. 100
25. 1,000

26. 514,000   27. 680,000
28. 100; 135; 45   29. 5; 850; 5; 170
30. 100; 8,400; 2,100   31. 1,000; 924; 154
32. 9; 981; 9; 109   33. 1,000; 756; 108
34. 31   35. 152

Lesson 2.6

1. 4   2. 5 R 10
3. 3 R 1   4. 11 R 48
5. 8 R 14   6. 7 R 2
7. 21 R 15   8. 18 R 21
9. Estimated quotient = 80
   Actual quotient = 79
10. Estimated quotient = 60
   Actual quotient = 65
11. Estimated quotient = 100
   Actual quotient = 106
12. Estimated quotient = 80
   Actual quotient = 82
13. Estimated quotient = 100
   Actual quotient = 99
14. Estimated quotient = 40
   Actual quotient = 38
15. Estimated quotient = 30
   Actual quotient = 26
16. Estimated quotient = 20
   Actual quotient = 19

Lesson 2.7

1. 110
   Step 1 $60 - 20 = 40$
   Step 2 $40 + 70 = 110$
2. 280
   Step 1 $200 \div 5 = 40$
   Step 2 $40 \times 7 = 280$
3. 82
   Step 1 $135 \div 3 = 45$
   Step 2 $100 - 45 = 55$
   Step 3 $55 + 27 = 82$
4. 200
   Step 1 $108 \div 9 = 12$
   Step 2 $12 \times 10 = 120$
   Step 3 $80 + 120 = 200$

5. 411
   Step 1 $42 \times 10 = 420$
   Step 2 $72 \div 8 = 9$
   Step 3 $420 - 9 = 411$
6. 18
   Step 1 $38 - 18 = 20$
   Step 2 $90 \times 20 = 1,800$
   Step 3 $1,800 \div 100 = 18$
7. 0
   Step 1 $80 \div 2 = 40$
   Step 2 $100 - 40 = 60$
   Step 3 $15 \times 4 = 60$
   Step 4 $60 - 60 = 0$
8. 102   9. 422
10. 32   11. 695
12. 204   13. 334
14. 33   15. 124
16. 20   17. 288
18. 1   19. 45
20. 6

	Expression	Order
21.	$34 \times 3 \div 6 = 17$	× ÷
22.	$184 + 27 \times 3 = 265$	× +
23.	$100 - 68 + 37 \times 4 = 180$	× − +
24.	$19 \times 4 + 84 \div 6 = 90$	× ÷ +
25.	$7 + 47 \times 8 \div 4 - 28 = 73$	× ÷ + −
26.	$30 - (45 - 17) = 2$	(−) −
27.	$7 \times (14 + 26) \div 8 = 35$	(+) × ÷
28.	$(73 + 27) - 136 \div 4 = 66$	(+) ÷ −

Lesson 2.8

1. $1,456 \div 56 = 26$
   $26 \times \$18 = \$468$
   He collects \$468.
2. $230 - 50 = 180$
   $180 \div 15 = 12$
   $12 \times \$20 = \$240$
   Each child collected \$240.
3. $641 + 490 = 1,131$
   $1,131 \times 8 = 9,048$
   $9,048 \div 58 = 156$
   There are 156 art pieces in each classroom.

4. $487 + 345 = 832$
   $832 - 40 = 792$
   $792 \div 36 = 22$

   There are 22 seashells in each box.

5. $\$4 + 3 \times \$7 = \$25$

   He paid \$25.

6. Cost of tickets for 1 adult and 3 children
   $= \$7 + 3 \times \$3$
   $= \$16$

   $\$6,000 \div \$16 = 375$
   $375 \times 4 = 1,500$

   1,500 people bought tickets.

7.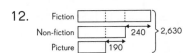

   9 units $\longrightarrow$ \$324
   1 unit $\longrightarrow$ $\$324 \div 9 = \$36$
   3 units $\longrightarrow$ $3 \times \$36 = \$108$

   The cost of the handbag is \$108.

8.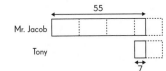

   $(55 - 7) \div 3 = 16$
   $16 - 7 = 9$

   In 9 years, Mr. Jacob will be 4 times as old as Tony.

9.

   3 video cameras, 5 digital cameras, \$3,213

   1 unit $\longrightarrow$ $\$3,213 \div 17 = \$189$
   5 units $\longrightarrow$ $5 \times \$189 = \$945$

   He pays \$945.

10. Anne, Ryan, Joel, 1,925

    7 units $\longrightarrow$ 1,925
    1 unit $\longrightarrow$ $1,925 \div 7 = 275$
    4 units $\longrightarrow$ $4 \times 275 = 1,100$

    Joel collects 1,100 cans.

11.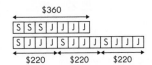

    4 units $\longrightarrow$ $328 - 176 = 152$
    1 unit $\longrightarrow$ $152 \div 4 = 38$
    $176 - 38 = 138$

    David has 138 marbles.

12. Fiction, Non-fiction 240, Picture 190, 2,630

    3 units $\longrightarrow$ $2,630 - 240 - 190 - 190$
    $= 2,010$

    1 unit $\longrightarrow$ $2,010 \div 3 = 670$
    $670 + 190 = 860$
    $860 + 240 = 1,100$

    There are 670 picture books, 860 non-fiction books, and 1,100 fiction books.

13.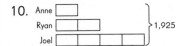

    49 m
    Blue Blue Yellow Blue Blue Yellow Yellow Yellow Yellow
    Blue Blue Yellow
    17 m

    Length of 3 yellow banners
    $= 49 - 17 - 17 = 15$ m
    Length of 1 yellow banner $= 15 \div 3$
    $= 5$ m
    Length of 1 blue banner $= (17 - 5) \div 2$
    $= 6$ m

    The length of each blue banner is 6 meters.

14. S: shirt, J: jacket

    \$360
    S S S J J J J
    S J J J S J J J S J J J
    \$220   \$220   \$220

    Cost of 3 shirts and 9 jackets
    $= 3 \times \$220$
    $= \$660$

    Cost of 5 jackets $= \$660 - \$360$
    $= \$300$

    Cost of 1 jacket $= \$300 \div 5$
    $= \$60$

    Cost of 1 shirt $= \$220 - (\$60 \times 3)$
    $= \$40$

    The cost of each shirt is \$40.

15.

Day	Amount More Than First Day (g)
1	
2	1 × 20
3	2 × 20
4	3 × 20
5	4 × 20
6	5 × 20
7	6 × 20
Total	21 × 20 = 420

(1,260 − 420) ÷ 7 = 120

The hamsters ate 120 grams of food on the first day.

16.
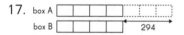

1 unit ➞ $198 + $20 − $60 = $158

$158 × 2 − $20 = $296

Ann had $296 at first.

17.

3 units ➞ 294

1 unit ➞ 294 ÷ 3 = 98

7 units ➞ 7 × 98 = 686

There were 686 marbles in box A at first.

Put on Your Thinking Cap!

1. Strategy: Use guess and check

    Solution:

No. of Correct Answers	No. of Incorrect Answers	Score
15	5	75 − 10 = 65
14	6	70 − 12 = 58
13	7	65 − 14 = 51

    She has 13 correct answers.

2. Strategy: Use guess and check

    Solution: Estimate the number. Then guess and check your answer.

    20 × 20 = 400

    30 × 30 = 900

    624 is in between 400 and 900. So the two numbers are greater than 20 but less than 30.

    The last digit of the product 624 is

    4 ➞ 4 × 6 = 24.

    24 × 26 = 624

    The greater number is 26.

3. Thinking skill: Identifying patterns and relationships

    Strategy: Look for pattern

Solution: 264; 385; 792; 759; 638; 836

There is a pattern in the answers. To find the answers without using a calculator, follow these steps:

Step 1 Separate the digits of the first factor.
For example, 69 × 11 ➞ 6 9.

Step 2 Add the digits of the first factor.
For example, 6 + 9 = 15.

Step 3 Put the ones digit of the sum from Step 2 between the digits in Step 1.
For example, 6**5**9.

Step 4 Add the tens digit of the sum from Step 2 to the hundreds digit of the number in Step 3.
For example, **7**59.

4. Thinking skill: Comparing

    Strategies: Use a model, Use before-after concept

    Solution:

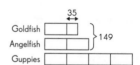

    8 units ➞ 976

    1 unit ➞ 976 ÷ 8 = 122

    5 units ➞ 5 × 122 = 610

    Benga should give Aaron 610 cards.

5. Thinking skill: Comparing

    Strategies: Use a model, Use before-after concept

    Solution:

    3 units ➞ 149 − 35 = 114

    1 unit ➞ 114 ÷ 3 = 38

    7 units ➞ 7 × 38 = 266

    266 fish are left in the aquarium.

6. Thinking skill: Comparing

    Strategy: Use guess and check

    Solution: Common multiples of 5 and 7 are 35, 70, 105, ...

No. of Fruits	Cost of Oranges	Cost of Pears	Difference in Amount
35	(35 ÷ 7) × $2 = $10	(35 ÷ 5) × $3 = $21	$11
70	(70 ÷ 7) × $2 = $20	(70 ÷ 5) × $3 = $42	$22
105	(105 ÷ 7) × $2 = $30	(105 ÷ 5) × $3 = $63	$33

a. $30 + $63 = $93
   Sophia pays $93 in all.
b. 2 × 105 = 210
   She buys 210 oranges and pears altogether.

7. Thinking skill: Comparing

   Strategies: Use a model, Use before-after concept

   Solution:

   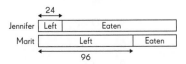

   Difference in number of crackers left
   = 96 − 24
   = 72

   Difference in number of crackers eaten
   each day = 6

   Number of days = 72 ÷ 6
                  = 12

   12 × 12 + 96 = 240

   Each of them had 240 crackers at first.

8. Thinking skill: Comparing

   Strategies: Use a model, Use before-after concept

   Solution:

   | Robert | Left | Left | Left | Left | Spent |
   | Damien | Left | Spent |
   $12

   Difference in amount left = 3 × $12
                             = $36

   Difference in spending in each day
   = $6 − $4
   = $2

   Number of days = $36 ÷ $2
                  = 18

   18 × $6 + $12 = $120

   Each boy had $120 at first.

9. Thinking skill: Identifying patterns and
                   relationships

   Solution:

   80 ÷ (5 + 1) = 13 R 2
   80 − 13 = 67

   The least number of highlighters is 67.

10. Thinking skill: Identifying patterns and
                    relationships

    Strategies: Work backward, Use guess and check

Solution:
a. Work backward to find the greatest factor
   of 54, 108 and 189.

   54 = 2 × 27
   108 = 4 × 27
   189 = 7 × 27

   The length of each piece of cut rope is
   27 centimeters.
b. 2 + 4 + 7 = 13
   Benita gets 13 pieces of cut rope.

11. Thinking skill: Analyzing parts and whole

    Strategy: Use a diagram

    Solution:

    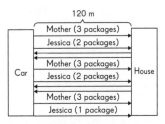

    10 × 120 = 1,200

    The total distance covered was 1,200 meters.

12. Thinking skill: Identifying patterns and relationships

    Strategy: Use guess and check

    Solution:

    Greatest: 542 × 63 = 34,146

    Least: 356 × 24 = 8,544

Chapter 3

Lesson 3.1

1. Answers vary.
   Samples: $\frac{2}{8}$; $\frac{3}{12}$

2. Answers vary.
   Samples: $\frac{4}{6}$; $\frac{6}{9}$

3. Answers vary.
   Samples: $\frac{8}{18}$; $\frac{12}{27}$

4. Answers vary.
   Samples: $\frac{6}{10}$; $\frac{9}{15}$

5. Answers vary.
   Samples: $\frac{12}{14}$; $\frac{18}{21}$

6. Answers vary.

   Samples: $\frac{10}{16}$; $\frac{15}{24}$

7.

   $$\frac{2}{3} + \frac{1}{4} = \frac{8}{12} + \frac{3}{12}$$
   $$= \frac{11}{12}$$

8.

   $$\frac{2}{5} + \frac{1}{2} = \frac{4}{10} + \frac{5}{10}$$
   $$= \frac{9}{10}$$

9. 1; $\frac{31}{40}$

10. $\frac{1}{2}$; $\frac{13}{30}$

11. $1\frac{1}{2}$; $1\frac{9}{20}$

12. 2; $1\frac{7}{15}$

13. 1; $1\frac{1}{24}$

14. 2; $1\frac{17}{28}$

Lesson 3.2

1.

   $$\frac{4}{5} - \frac{1}{2} = \frac{8}{10} - \frac{5}{10} = \frac{3}{10}$$

2.

   $$\frac{4}{9} - \frac{1}{6} = \frac{8}{18} - \frac{3}{18} = \frac{5}{18}$$

3. $\frac{1}{2}$; $\frac{7}{15}$

4. $\frac{1}{2}$; $\frac{1}{12}$

5. 0; $\frac{1}{72}$

6. $\frac{1}{2}$; $\frac{1}{3}$

7. $\frac{1}{2}$; $\frac{11}{24}$

8. $\frac{1}{2}$; $\frac{7}{18}$

Lesson 3.3

1. $\frac{3}{5}$

2. $\frac{5}{2}$; $2\frac{1}{2}$

3. $\frac{3}{25}$

4. $\frac{2}{19}$

5. $7\frac{5}{7}$

6. $5\frac{1}{3}$

7. $4\frac{1}{2}$

8. $3\frac{1}{3}$

9. $5\frac{1}{2}$

10. $4\frac{2}{3}$

Lesson 3.4

1. 0.9

2. 0.8

3. 0.15

4. 0.36

5. 2.3

6. 2.5

7. 2.75

8. 3.6

9. 0.68

10. 3.75

11. 2.6

12. 3.875

13. 4.35

14. 5.75

15. $15 ÷ 6 = $2.50

    She pays $2.50 for each notebook.

Lesson 3.5

1. $5\frac{7}{8}$

2. $4\frac{5}{12}$

3. $5\frac{13}{24}$

4. $3\frac{11}{36}$

5. $7\frac{19}{24}$

6. $6\frac{11}{30}$

7. $3\frac{1}{2}$

8. $10\frac{1}{2}$

9. $3\frac{1}{2}$

10. 7

11. $6\frac{1}{2}$

12. 19

Lesson 3.6

1. $2\frac{5}{9}$

2. $1\frac{1}{4}$

3. $2\frac{7}{20}$

4. $4\frac{5}{24}$

5. $\frac{13}{21}$

6. $1\frac{7}{18}$

7. 2

8. $4\frac{1}{2}$

9. $\frac{1}{2}$

10. 2

11. 2

12. $1\frac{1}{2}$

Lesson 3.7

1. a. $28 ÷ 8 = 3\frac{1}{2}$

   It takes $3\frac{1}{2}$ minutes to play 1 song.

b. $3\frac{1}{2} = 3.5$

It takes 3.5 minutes to play 1 song.

2. $\frac{1}{4} + \frac{1}{6} = \frac{5}{12}$

$1 - \frac{5}{12} = \frac{7}{12}$

$\frac{7}{12}$ of the participants have black hair.

3. $3\frac{7}{10} + 2\frac{3}{4} = 6\frac{9}{20}$

$6\frac{9}{20} - 4\frac{3}{5} = 1\frac{17}{20} = 1.85$

1.85 pounds of flour are left.

4. $2\frac{3}{4} - \frac{5}{8} = 2\frac{1}{8}$

$2\frac{3}{4} + 2\frac{1}{8} = 4\frac{7}{8} = 4.875$

She uses 4.875 meters of cloth in all.

5. $7 \times \frac{1}{6} = \frac{7}{6}$

$1\frac{8}{9} - \frac{7}{6} = \frac{13}{18}$

$\frac{13}{18}$ liter of apple juice is left after a week.

6. $\frac{1}{8} + \frac{1}{6} + \frac{1}{6} + \frac{1}{6} = \frac{5}{8}$

$1 - \frac{5}{8} = \frac{3}{8}$

$\frac{3}{8}$ of the loaf of bread is left.

7. $\frac{2}{9} + \frac{1}{6} + \frac{2}{6} = \frac{13}{18}$

$1 - \frac{13}{18} = \frac{5}{18}$

$\frac{5}{18}$ of the book is not read.

8. a. $1\frac{2}{3} + \frac{7}{8} = 2\frac{13}{24}$

Jamal spent $2\frac{13}{24}$ hours watching television and helping with housework.

b. $1\frac{4}{5} - \frac{7}{8} = \frac{37}{40}$

Jamal spent $\frac{37}{40}$ hour more on the nap.

9. $2\frac{3}{5} + \frac{3}{4} = 3\frac{7}{20}$

$3\frac{7}{20} + 2\frac{3}{5} = 5\frac{19}{20}$

They buy $5\frac{19}{20}$ pounds of meat altogether.

10. $1\frac{7}{10} - \frac{1}{4} = 1\frac{9}{20}$

$1\frac{7}{10} + 1\frac{9}{20} = 3\frac{3}{20}$

The total weight of the two boxes is $3\frac{3}{20}$ pounds.

11. $4\frac{3}{5} - \frac{3}{4} = 3\frac{17}{20}$

$4\frac{3}{5} + 4\frac{3}{5} + 3\frac{17}{20} + 3\frac{17}{20} = 16\frac{9}{10}$

The perimeter of the storeroom is $16\frac{9}{10}$ meters.

12. $4\frac{1}{5} + 3\frac{2}{5} = 7\frac{3}{5}$

$7\frac{3}{5} - 2\frac{1}{2} = 5\frac{1}{10}$

There were $5\frac{1}{10}$ liters of water in the tank at first.

Put on Your Thinking Cap!

1. Thinking skill: Comparing

Solution:

Length of each piece of rope P

$= 2 \div 3 = \frac{2}{3}$ m

Length of each piece of rope Q

$= \frac{2}{3} + \frac{2}{5}$

$= 1\frac{1}{15}$ m

Length of rope Q $= 1\frac{1}{15} + 1\frac{1}{15} + 1\frac{1}{15}$

$= 3\frac{1}{5}$

The length of rope Q is $3\frac{1}{5}$ meters.

2. Thinking skill: Comparing

Strategy: Use a model

Solution:

Vivian has 12 units of money and Lionel has 3 units.

$12 \div 3 = 4$

Vivian's amount of money is 4 times Lionel's amount of money.

3. Thinking skill: Comparing

Strategy: Use a model

Solution:

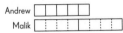

Andrew's savings is $\frac{5}{8}$ of Malik's savings.

4. Thinking skill: Identifying patterns and relationships

Strategy: Look for pattern

Solution:

$$\frac{1}{100} + \frac{2}{100} + \cdots + \frac{49}{100} + \frac{50}{100} + \frac{51}{100} + \cdots + \frac{98}{100} + \frac{99}{100}$$

The sum of each pair of fractions is 1.
Number of such pairs of fractions
$= 98 \div 2$
$= 49$
Value $= 49 + \frac{50}{100}$
$\qquad = 49\frac{1}{2}$

5. Thinking skill: Identifying patterns and relationships

Strategy: Look for pattern

Solution:
Look for pairs of numbers that give a sum of 11.
$1 + 2 + 3 + 4 + 5 + 6 + 7 + 8 + 9 + 10$
$= 5 \times 11$
$= 55$

Value
$= \frac{1}{99} \times 55$
$= \frac{5}{9}$

6. Thinking skill: Identifying patterns and relationships

Strategy: Look for pattern

Solution:

$$\frac{1}{1 \times 2} + \frac{1}{2 \times 3} = \frac{2}{3}$$

$$\frac{1}{1 \times 2} + \frac{1}{2 \times 3} + \frac{1}{3 \times 4} = \frac{3}{4}$$

$$\frac{1}{1 \times 2} + \frac{1}{2 \times 3} + \frac{1}{3 \times 4} + \frac{1}{4 \times 5} = \frac{4}{5}$$

$$\frac{1}{1 \times 2} + \frac{1}{2 \times 3} + \frac{1}{3 \times 4} + \cdots + \frac{1}{28 \times 29}$$
$$+ \frac{1}{29 \times 30} = \frac{29}{30}$$

7. Thinking skill: Comparing

Strategy: Use a model

Solution:

$$\frac{2}{5} = \frac{4}{10}; \frac{1}{2} = \frac{5}{10}$$

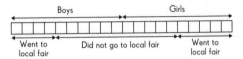

$\frac{11}{20}$ of the students in the class did not go to the local fair.

8. Thinking skill: Comparing

Strategy: Use a model

Solution:

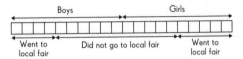

$\frac{3}{12} = \frac{1}{4}$

Sean gets $\frac{1}{4}$ of the marbles.

Chapter 4

Lesson 4.1

1. $\frac{1}{2}; \frac{3}{5}; \frac{3}{10}$
2. $\frac{3}{4}; \frac{5}{7}; \frac{15}{28}$
3. $\frac{15}{22}$
4. $\frac{7}{18}$
5. $\frac{5}{8}$
6. $\frac{4}{5}$
7. $\frac{1}{5}$
8. $\frac{1}{2}$

Lesson 4.2

1. $\frac{2}{7} \times \frac{3}{4} = \frac{3}{14}$

$\frac{3}{14} \times 56 = 12$

Rahul gets 12 paper clips.

2. $1 - \frac{2}{3} = \frac{1}{3}$

$\frac{1}{3} \times \frac{9}{10} = \frac{3}{10}$

$\frac{3}{10}$ hour is left.

3. **Method 1**

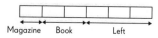

Magazine   Book   Left

$\frac{3}{6} = \frac{1}{2}$

$\frac{1}{2}$ of his savings are left.

Method 2

$1 - \frac{1}{6} = \frac{5}{6}$

$\frac{2}{5} \times \frac{5}{6} = \frac{1}{3}$

$1 - \frac{1}{6} - \frac{1}{3} = \frac{1}{2}$

$\frac{1}{2}$ of his savings are left.

4. Fraction of hats that are not red or blue

$= 1 - \frac{1}{6} - \frac{1}{3}$

$= \frac{1}{2}$

Fraction of hats that are green

$= \frac{3}{7} \times \frac{1}{2}$

$= \frac{3}{14}$

3 units → 27
1 unit → 27 ÷ 3 = 9
14 units → 14 × 9 = 126

There are 126 hats altogether.

5. $1 - \frac{1}{5} = \frac{4}{5}$

$\frac{7}{8} \times \frac{4}{5} = \frac{7}{10}$

$\frac{7}{10} \times 30 = 21$

She receives 21 text messages.

6. $1 - \frac{2}{5} = \frac{3}{5}$

$\frac{4}{9} \times \frac{3}{5} = \frac{4}{15}$

$\frac{3}{5} - \frac{4}{15} = \frac{5}{15} = \frac{1}{3}$

1 unit → 15
3 units → 3 × 15 = 45

Sam makes 45 bread rolls.

7.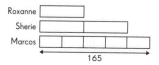

Devi
Anne
24

6 × 24 = 144

Anne has 144 cards.

8. **Method 1**

$\frac{4}{5} \times 165 = 132$

$132 ÷ 2 = 66$

$165 - 66 = 99$

Marcos has 99 more beads than Roxanne.

Method 2

Roxanne
Sherie
Marcos
165

5 units → 165
1 unit → 165 ÷ 5 = 33
3 units → 3 × 33 = 99

Marcos has 99 more beads than Roxanne.

9. $\frac{1}{5} = \frac{2}{10}$

$\frac{1}{2} = \frac{5}{10}$

$1 - \frac{1}{5} - \frac{1}{2} = \frac{3}{10}$

Dictionary $21   Left

3 units → $21
1 unit → $21 ÷ 3 = $7
5 units → 5 × $7 = $35

Ken has $35 left.

10. a.

Spent   Left

4 units → $24
1 unit → $24 ÷ 4 = $6
5 units → 5 × $6 = $30

She spends $30.

b.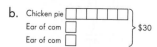

Chicken pie
Ear of corn
Ear of corn
$30

8 units → $30
1 unit → $30 ÷ 8 = $3.75
6 units → 6 × $3.75 = $22.50

The chicken pie costs $22.50.

11.
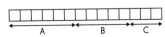

$$7 \text{ units} \longrightarrow 98$$
$$1 \text{ unit} \longrightarrow 98 \div 7 = 14$$
$$5 \text{ units} \longrightarrow 5 \times 14 = 70 \text{ (gave away)}$$
$$98 + 70 = 168$$

Melody must buy 168 more stickers.

12. $1 - \dfrac{3}{7} = \dfrac{4}{7}$

Fraction of biscuits in container B

$= \dfrac{5}{8} \times \dfrac{4}{7}$

$= \dfrac{5}{14}$

Fraction of biscuits in container C

$= 1 - \dfrac{3}{7} - \dfrac{5}{14}$

$= \dfrac{3}{14}$

Container A has 3 more units than container C.
$$3 \text{ units} \longrightarrow 21$$
$$1 \text{ unit} \longrightarrow 21 \div 3 = 7$$
$$14 \text{ units} \longrightarrow 14 \times 7 = 98$$

Jacky bakes 98 biscuits.

Lesson 4.3

1. $\dfrac{15}{16}$ 2. $\dfrac{7}{6}$ or $1\dfrac{1}{6}$

3. $\dfrac{20}{20}$ or 1   4. $\dfrac{15}{4}$ or $3\dfrac{3}{4}$

5. $\dfrac{10}{3}$ or $3\dfrac{1}{3}$ 6. $\dfrac{40}{3}$ or $13\dfrac{1}{3}$

7. $1\dfrac{1}{8}$ 8. $1\dfrac{1}{5}$

9. $1\dfrac{1}{3}$ 10. $1\dfrac{1}{14}$

11. $\dfrac{9}{14}$ 12. $\dfrac{9}{10}$

13. 6   14. $3\dfrac{3}{16}$

15. $5\dfrac{3}{5}$ 16. $2\dfrac{2}{3}$

17. $2\dfrac{2}{9}$ 18. $2\dfrac{7}{16}$

Lesson 4.4

1. $7\dfrac{3}{5}$ 2. 22

3. $8\dfrac{2}{3}$ 4. 39

5. 105   6. $20\dfrac{2}{3}$

7. $62\dfrac{1}{3}$ 8. $38\dfrac{6}{7}$

9. $30\dfrac{2}{3}$ 10. $33\dfrac{3}{4}$

11. $46\dfrac{1}{5}$ 12. $25\dfrac{1}{2}$

13. 10   14. 40, 8, 24, 24

15. 49, 7, 28, 28   16. $\dfrac{5}{8} \times 64 = 40$

17. 50   18. 24

19. 42   20. 16

21. 30   22. 56

23. $\dfrac{3}{8} \times 32 = 12$

Lesson 4.5

1. $1\dfrac{4}{5} \times 7 = 12\dfrac{3}{5}$

$12\dfrac{3}{5}$ is about 13.

$13 \div 2 = 6\dfrac{1}{2}$

Mrs. Smith needs to buy 7 bottles every week.

2. $1\dfrac{3}{4} \times 9 = 15\dfrac{3}{4}$

$15\dfrac{3}{4}$ yards are about 16 yards.

Lily needs 16 yards of ribbon.

3.
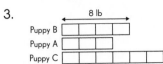

$$4 \text{ units} \longrightarrow 8 \text{ lb}$$
$$1 \text{ unit} \longrightarrow 2 \text{ lb}$$
$$6 \text{ units} \longrightarrow 12 \text{ lb}$$

The weight of puppy C is 12 pounds.

4. Area of flowerbed = $3\frac{3}{4} \times 2$

$\qquad\qquad\qquad = 7\frac{1}{2}$ m²

Area of flowerbed with border

$= (3\frac{3}{4} + \frac{1}{2} + \frac{1}{2}) \times (2 + \frac{1}{2} + \frac{1}{2})$

$= 4\frac{3}{4} \times 3$

$= 14\frac{1}{4}$ m²

Area of border $= 14\frac{1}{4} - 7\frac{1}{2}$

$\qquad\qquad\qquad = 6\frac{3}{4}$ m²

Cost $= 6\frac{3}{4} \times \$20$

$\qquad = \$135$

Uncle James has to pay \$135.

Lesson 4.6

1. $\frac{1}{6}, \frac{1}{6}$

2.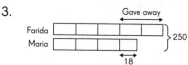

   $\frac{1}{12}$

3.
   $\frac{1}{9}$

4. $\frac{2}{15}$ 5. $\frac{1}{24}$

6. $\frac{3}{10}$ 7. $\frac{1}{18}$

8. $3 \div \frac{1}{4} = 12$ 9. $4 \div \frac{1}{3} = 12$

10. 8   11. 24

12. 15   13. 10

14. 12   15. 24

16. 21   17. 36

18. $\frac{5}{12} \div 5 = \frac{1}{12}$

   There is $\frac{1}{12}$ gallon of paint in each pot.

19. $\frac{1}{2} \div 5 = \frac{1}{10}$

   Each girl has $\frac{1}{10}$ of the loaf of bread.

20. $\frac{9}{10} \div 6 = \frac{3}{20}$

   $\frac{3}{20} + \frac{3}{20} = \frac{3}{10}$

   The total length of 2 of the pieces is $\frac{3}{10}$ yard.

21. $1 - \frac{1}{5} = \frac{4}{5}$

   $\frac{4}{5} \div 3 = \frac{4}{15}$

   Each friend got $\frac{4}{15}$ of the bag of nuts.

22. a. 1 L $\div 4 = \frac{1}{4}$ L

   Each of her children got $\frac{1}{4}$ liter of the milk.

   $\frac{1}{4}$ L $\div 5 = \frac{1}{20}$ L

   Each kitten drank $\frac{1}{20}$ liter of the milk.

   b. 1L $= 1,000$ mL

   $\frac{1}{20} \times 1,000 = 50$ mL

   Each kitten got 50 milliliters.

Lesson 4.7

1. $3 \div \frac{1}{4} = 12$

   She will use up the flour in 12 days.

2. $4 \div \frac{1}{5} = 20$

   She can make 20 batches of pancakes.

3.

   Farida / Maria — Gave away — 250 — 18

Method 1

8 units → $250 - 18 = 232$

1 unit → $232 \div 8 = 29$

$3 \times 29 + 18 = 105$

Maria had 105 beads at first.

Method 2

$250 - 18 = 232$

$\frac{3}{8} \times 232 = 87$

$87 + 18 = 105$

Maria had 105 beads at first.

4. Paul / Shawn / Tim — 280

10 units → 280

1 unit → $280 \div 10 = 28$

3 units → $3 \times 28 = 84$

Tim has 84 more postcards than Paul.

5. $1 - \dfrac{5}{9} = \dfrac{4}{9}$

Number of boys who do not take part in sports activities

$= \dfrac{4}{9} \times 540$

$= 240$

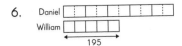

Number of boys in school

$= \dfrac{3}{5} \times 1{,}800$

$= 1{,}080$

Number of boys who take part in sports activities

$= 1{,}080 - 240$

$= 840$

840 boys take part in sports activities.

6.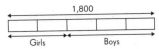

5 units $\longrightarrow$ 195

10 units $\longrightarrow$ 195 $\times$ 2 = 390

Daniel has 390 marbles.

7.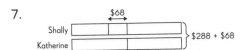

4 units $\longrightarrow$ $288 + $68 = $356

1 unit $\longrightarrow$ $356 ÷ 4 = $89

$89 − $68 = $21

Shally had $21 at first.

8.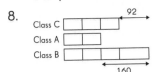

1 unit $\longrightarrow$ 160 − 92 = 68

2 units $\longrightarrow$ 2 × 68 = 136

136 + 160 = 296

Class B folds 296 paper cranes.

9.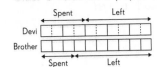

6 + 7 = 13

13 units $\longrightarrow$ $78

1 unit $\longrightarrow$ $78 ÷ 13 = $6

7 units $\longrightarrow$ 7 × $6 = $42

They spent $42 altogether.

10.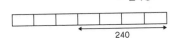

7 units $\longrightarrow$ $80 − $17 = $63

1 unit $\longrightarrow$ $63 ÷ 7 = $9

$9 + $17 = $26

Emily had $26 more than Sarah at first.

11. Number of girls $= \dfrac{3}{8} \times 40$

$= 15$

Number of boys $= 40 - 15$

$= 25$

$(15 \times 2) + (25 \times 1) = 55$

55 units $\longrightarrow$ 220

1 unit $\longrightarrow$ 220 ÷ 55 = 4

$(15 \times 2) - 25 = 5$

5 units $\longrightarrow$ 5 × 4 = 20

All the girls receive 20 more balloons than all the boys.

12. Number of nickels $= 1{,}200 ÷ 5$

$= 240$

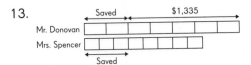

4 units $\longrightarrow$ 240

1 unit $\longrightarrow$ 240 ÷ 4 = 60

7 units $\longrightarrow$ 7 × 60 = 420

There are 420 coins in the piggy bank.

13.

Mr. Donovan:

5 units $\longrightarrow$ $1,335

1 unit $\longrightarrow$ $1,335 ÷ 5 = $267

2 units $\longrightarrow$ 2 × $267 = $534

Mrs. Spencer:

3 units $\longrightarrow$ $534

1 unit $\longrightarrow$ $534 ÷ 3 = $178

8 units $\longrightarrow$ 8 × $178 = $1,424

Mrs. Spencer's paycheck is $1,424.

14.

40 units $\longrightarrow$ $12

5 units $\longrightarrow$ $12 ÷ 8 = $1.50

The cost of 1 pound of sugar was $1.50.

Put on Your Thinking Cap!

1. Thinking skill: Comparing

   Strategy: Use a model

   Solution:

   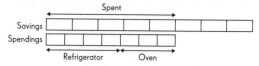

   1 unit → $280

   7 units → 7 × $280 = $1,960

   5 units → $1,960

   1 unit → $1,960 ÷ 5 = $392

   8 units → 8 × $392 = $3,136

   Mrs. Tan's savings was $3,136 at first.

2. Thinking skill: Comparing

   Strategy: Use a model

   Solution:

   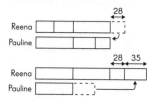

   1 unit → 28 + 35 = 63

   3 units → 3 × 63 = 189

   189 − 35 = 154

   Reena has 154 bookmarks.

3. Thinking skill: Comparing

   Strategies: Use a model, Use before-after concept

   Solution:

   $\frac{3}{4} = \frac{9}{12}$, $\frac{1}{6} = \frac{2}{12}$

   7 units → $203

   1 unit → $203 ÷ 7 = $29

   12 units → 12 × $29 = $348

   Kerrie had $348.

4. Strategies: Use a model, Use before-after concept

   Solution:

   Before:

   Number of girls = $\frac{3}{5}$ × 120 = 72

   Number of boys = 120 − 72 = 48

   After:

   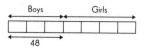

   3 units → 48

   1 unit → 48 ÷ 3 = 16

   4 units → 4 × 16 = 64

   72 − 64 = 8

   8 girls left the library.

5. Thinking skill: Comparing

   Strategy: Use before-after concept

   Solution:

   Before:

   Adults → 3 units ⎫ Difference

   Children → 5 units ⎭ = 2 units

   After:

   Adults → 2 units × 2 = 4 units ⎫ Difference

   Children → 3 units × 2 = 6 units ⎭ = 2 units

   4 units − 3 units = 1 unit

   1 unit → 6

   8 units → 8 × 6 = 48

   48 people were on the bus at first.

6. Strategies: Use a model, Use before-after concept

   Solution:

   Before:

   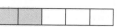

   After:

   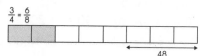

   3 units → 48

   1 unit → 48 ÷ 3 = 16

   5 units → 5 × 16 = 80

   There were 80 counters in the box at first.

7. Thinking skill: Comparing

Strategies: Use a model, Use before-after concept

Solution:

Before:

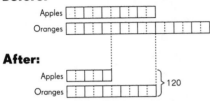

After:

15 units → 120

1 unit → 120 ÷ 15 = 8

26 units → 26 × 8 = 208

There were 208 apples and oranges at the stand at first.

8. Thinking skill: Comparing

Strategy: Use before-after concept

Solution:

After:

In puzzle → 13 units ⎫
Not in puzzle → 7 units ⎬ Total = 20 units

Before:

In puzzle → 2 units × 4 = 8 units ⎫
Not in puzzle → 3 units × 4 = 12 units ⎬ Total = 20 units

12 units − 7 units = 5 units

5 units → 300

1 unit → 300 ÷ 5 = 60

20 units → 20 × 60 = 1,200

The jigsaw puzzle consists of 1,200 pieces.

9. Thinking skill: Analyzing parts and whole

Strategy: Work backward

Solution:

720 ÷ 2 = 360

Each had 360 stamps in the end.

	Samuel	Pat
Finally	360	360 ($\frac{2}{3}$ left)
Pat to Samuel	360 − 180 = 180 ($\frac{3}{4}$ left)	360 ÷ 2 = 180 360 + 180 = 540
Samuel to Pat	180 ÷ 3 = 60 180 + 60 = 240	540 − 60 = 480

Samuel had 240 stamps at first.

10. Thinking skill: Analyzing parts and whole

Strategy: Work backward

Solution:

Stage	Work	A	B	C
Finally		18 gal	18 gal	18 gal
C to A	Pail C: 18 ÷ 3 × 4 = 24 Pail A: 18 − 6 = 12	12 gal	18 gal	24 gal
B to C	Pail B: 18 ÷ 3 × 4 = 24 Pail C: 24 − 6 = 18	12 gal	24 gal	18 gal
A to B	Pail A: 12 ÷ 3 × 4 = 16 Pail B: 24 − 4 = 20	16 gal	20 gal	18 gal

Pail A had 16 gallons of water,
pail B had 20 gallons of water, and
pail C had 18 gallons of water at first.

Test Prep for Chapters 1 to 4

1. C   2. C   3. A   4. C

5. D   6. B   7. D   8. B

9. A   10. C

11. 2,467,058   12. 710,000

13. 203,485

14. 3,190,500   3,090,500   2,090,500
319,500   290,500

15. 16   16. 424

17. $4\frac{7}{12}$ 18. 144

19. 5.925   20. $\frac{21}{40}$

21.

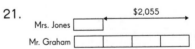

3 units → $2,055

1 unit → $2,055 ÷ 3 = $685

4 units → 4 × $685 = $2,740

Mr. Graham had $2,740.

22.

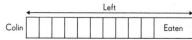

Difference in quantity left = 4 × 9
= 36

Difference in quantity eaten each day
= 8 − 5
= 3

Number of days = 36 ÷ 3
= 12

Number of cashews = 12 × 8 + 4
= 100

Each child had 100 cashews at first.

23.

Model planes $\boxed{}$
Model cars $\boxed{\ 3 \times \$38}$ $\Big\}\$834$

Cost of 1 model plane = $52 − $14
= $38

Cost of 1 model car and 1 model plane
= $52 + $38
= $90

$834 − 3 × $38 = $720

Number of model cars = $720 ÷ $90
= 8

Number of model planes = 8 + 3
= 11

He buys 11 model planes.

Chapter 5

Lesson 5.1

1. 125; 625; 3,125
   (1 × 5 = 5, 5 × 5 = 25, 25 × 5 = 125,
   125 × 5 = 625, 625 × 5 = 3,125)

2. 216; 343; 512
   (6 × 6 × 6 = 216, 7 × 7 × 7 = 343,
   8 × 8 × 8 = 512)

3. 30; 42; 56
   (2 + 4 = 6, 6 + 6 = 12, 12 + 8 = 20,
   20 + 10 = 30,   30 + 12 = 42,
   42 + 14 = 56)
   or
   (1 × 2 = 2, 2 × 3 = 6, 3 × 4 = 12,
   4 × 5 = 20, 5 × 6 = 30, 6 × 7 = 42,
   7 × 8 = 56)

4. 65; 62; 310
   (1 × 5 = 5, 5 − 2 = 3, 3 × 5 = 15,
   15 − 2 = 13, 13 × 5 = 65, 65 − 3 = 62
   62 × 5 = 310)

5. 13; 21; 34
   (1 + 1 = 2, 1 + 2 = 3, 2 + 3 = 5,
   3 + 5 = 8, 5 + 8 = 13, 8 + 13 = 21
   13 + 21 = 34)

Length of Side of Square (in.)	1	2	3	4	5	6
Area of Square (in.²)	1	4	9	16	25	36

6. a. 9 × 9 = 81 sq in.
   b. 12 × 12 = 144 sq in.

7. a. $\sqrt{64}$ = 8 in.   b. $\sqrt{100}$ = 10 in.

Number of Bags	1	2	3	4	5
Cost of Each ($)	2.50	5.00	7.50	10.00	12.50

8. a. $2.50 × 7 = $17.50
   b. $2.50 × 10 = $25

9. a. $20 ÷ 2.50 = 8 bags
   b. $37.50 ÷ 2.50 = 15 bags

Lesson 5.2

1. $w + 8$
2. $a − 10$
3. $p + \dfrac{3}{4}$
4. $5 − 6y$
5. $6g$
6. $\dfrac{3k}{2}$
7. $4h$
8. $5s − 12$
9. $7b + 8$
10. $\dfrac{5d}{4}$
11. 7
12. 13
13. 31
14. 60
15. 14
16. 37
17. 7
18. 5
19. 10
20. 9

21. Mrs. Smith pays 5x dollars.

22. Alyssa has (6p − 15) dollars more than her brother.

23. 2 × 7 = 14
    (5m − 14) liter of milk is left.

24. Each of them has $\dfrac{(3y + 8)}{2}$ comics.

25. k bottles of pasta sauce cost
$k \times \$4 = \$4k$.
He received $\$(10 - 4k)$ change.

26. The cost of 3 such books is $\dfrac{3y}{8}$ dollars.

27. John has $(y - 20)$ stickers for his sisters.
Each sister gets $\left(\dfrac{y - 20}{2}\right)$ stickers.

28. Kenny has $(m + 10)$ fish.
He buys another $(20 + 30) = 50$ fish.
Kenny has $(m + 60)$ fish now.

29. The shorter piece is $\left(\dfrac{g - 10}{2}\right)$ inches long.

Lesson 5.3

1. $3g$
2. $10w$
3. $5a$
4. $8b$
5. $7h$
6. $6k$
7. $11d$
8. $15n$
9. $12x - 4$
10. $6 + 10g$
11. $4n + 5$
12. $6d - 5$
13. $12 + 3k$
14. $7w + 3$
15. $4 + 13h$
16. $5 + 3m$
17. $5 + 3s$
18. $4n + 13$

Lesson 5.4

1. $<$
2. $=$
3. $>$
4. $>$
5. $>$
6. $<$
7. $>$
8. $=$
9. 7
10. 4
11. 6
12. 7
13. 8
14. 9

Lesson 5.5

1. a. Joan's brother is $(4y - 28)$ years old.
   b. $4 \times 12 - 28 = 20$
   Her brother is 20 years old.

2. a. The cost of renting the car is $\$(120 + 18n)$.
   b. $\$(120 + 18 \times 8) = \$264$
   The cost of renting the car is $264.

3. a. $\$5 = 500$ cents
   He spends $7g$ cents in one week.
   He has $(500 - 7g)$ cents left.
   b. $7g$ cents $= \dfrac{7g}{100}$ dollars

   He has $\left(5 - \dfrac{7g}{100}\right)$ dollars left.

4. a. $10w - 2w = 8w$
   $8w \div 2 = 4w$
   Cindy's age is $4w$ years.
   b. If $w = 4$,
   $4w = 4 \times 4 = 16$
   Cindy is 16 years old.

5. a. Patrick paid $3p$ dollars.
   b. $3p = 36$
   $p = 12$
   When $p = 12$, Patrick and Amanda paid the
   same amount of money for the planes.

6. a. $4k + 6 = 4 \times 5 + 6 = 26$
   $6k - 2 = 6 \times 5 - 2 = 28$
   $26 < 28$
   Nancy has a shorter ribbon.
   b. $6k - 2 = 4k + 6$
   $2k = 8$
   $k = 4$
   When $k = 4$, they will have the same length
   of ribbon.

7. $50b - 28b = 22b$
   $28b > 22b$
   No, he does not save more than he spends.

8. Benny has $3p$ game cards.
   Together Anne and Benny have
   $(p + 3p) = 4p$ game cards.
   If $4p > 30$, then p must be 8, 9, 10, ...
   The least value of p is 8 so that Anne and
   Benny together have more game cards than Colin.

Put on Your Thinking Cap!

1. Thinking skill: Analyzing parts and whole
   Strategy: Solve part of the problem
   Solution:
   $5 \times p = 5p$
   $200 \text{ g} \times 5 = 1,000 \text{ g} = 1 \text{ kg}$
   The total mass of the crackers in 5 boxes
   is $(5p - 1)$ kilograms.

2. Thinking skill: Analyzing parts and whole
   Strategy: Solve part of the problem
   Solution:
   a. Mr. Johnson will pay $\$(2x + 30)$.
   b. $2 \times 200 + 30 = 430$

   He will have to pay $430.

3. Thinking skill: Analyzing parts and whole

   Strategy: Solve part of the problem

   Solution:

   a. The remaining stickers are shared
      by 3 people.

      She gives each brother $\dfrac{(80 - 5m)}{3}$ stickers.

   b. If $m = 4$,

      $\dfrac{(80 - 5 \times 4)}{3} = 20$

      Each brother gets 20 stickers.

4. Thinking skill: Analyzing parts and whole

   Strategy: Solve part of the problem

   Solution:

   a. Jerry's allowance $= 3k$ dollars
      Danny's allowance $= (3k + 20)$ dollars
      $k + 3k + 3k + 20 = 7k + 20$

      Their total monthly allowance is
      $(7k + 20)$ dollars.

   b. $7 \times \$18 + \$20 = \$146$

      Their total monthly allowance is $146.

Chapter 6

Lesson 6.1

1. $\dfrac{4}{5} \times \dfrac{3}{8} = \dfrac{3}{10}$

   The area of the rectangle is $\dfrac{3}{10}$ square foot.

2. $\dfrac{20}{9} \times \dfrac{3}{5} = 1\dfrac{1}{3}$

   The area of the rectangle is $1\dfrac{1}{3}$ square inches.

3. $10\dfrac{1}{2} \times 6 = 63$

   The area of the rectangle is 63 square centimeters.

4. $20\dfrac{4}{5} \times 15 = 312$

   The area of the rectangle is 312 square meters.

Lesson 6.2

1. $\overline{AD}$
2. $\overline{BE}$
3. $\overline{CF}$
4. $\overline{QR}$
5. $\overline{PR}$
6. $\overline{PQ}$
7.
8.

9.
10.

11. Base $= \overline{KL}$, Height $= \overline{LM}$ or
    Base $= \overline{LM}$, Height $= \overline{KL}$
12. Base $= \overline{KL}$, Height $= \overline{VM}$ or
    Base $= \overline{LM}$, Height $= \overline{UK}$

Lesson 6.3

1. 324 in.²
2. 1,350 cm²
3. $346\dfrac{1}{2}$ ft²
4. $962\dfrac{1}{2}$ m²
5. 891 cm²
6. 900 in.²
7. 1,058 cm²
8. 1,944 ft²

Put on Your Thinking Cap!

1. Thinking skill: Spatial visualization

   Strategy: Simplify the problem

   Solution:

   Area of $ABC = \dfrac{1}{2} \times 72 \times 96$

   $= 3,456$ in.²

   Area of $ADC = \dfrac{1}{2} \times 72 \times 48$

   $= 1,728$ in.²

   Shaded area $= 3,456 - 1,728$

   $= 1,728$ in.²

2. Thinking skill: Spatial visualization

   Strategy: Simplify the problem

   Solution:

   Area of $ABCD = 60 \times 60$

   $= 3,600$ cm²

   Area of $ABC = \dfrac{1}{2} \times 60 \times 18$

   $= 540$ cm²

   Shaded area $= 3,600 - 2 \times 540$

   $= 2,520$ cm²

3. Thinking skill: Spatial visualization

Strategy: Simplify the problem

Solution:

Method 1

Base of 1 triangle $= 60 \div 5$
$$= 12 \text{ cm}$$

Height of 1 triangle $= 30 \div 2$
$$= 15 \text{ cm}$$

Area of 5 triangles $= 5 \times \frac{1}{2} \times 12 \times 15$
$$= 450 \text{ cm}^2$$

Area of remaining paper
$$= 60 \times 30 - 450$$
$$= 1,350 \text{ cm}^2$$

Method 2

Since the cut triangles make up a quarter of the paper,

area of the remaining paper
$$= \frac{3}{4} \times 60 \times 30$$
$$= 1,350 \text{ cm}^2$$

4. Thinking skill: Spatial visualization

Strategy: Simplify the problem

Solution:

Area of $BCD = \frac{1}{2} \times 24 \times 10$
$$= 120 \text{ cm}^2$$

Area of $BDE = \frac{1}{2} \times 26 \times 6$
$$= 78 \text{ cm}^2$$

Shaded area $= 120 - 78$
$$= 42 \text{ cm}^2$$

5. Thinking skill: Spatial visualization

Strategy: Simplify the problem

Solution:

Area of $PWTV = 36 \times 28$
$$= 1,008 \text{ ft}^2$$

Area of $PVU = \frac{1}{2} \times 24 \times 28$
$$= 336 \text{ ft}^2$$

Area of $QWSR = 24 \times 10$
$$= 240 \text{ ft}^2$$

Shaded area $= 1,008 - 336 - 240$
$$= 432 \text{ ft}^2$$

6. Thinking skill: Spatial visualization

Strategy: Simplify the problem

Solution:

$CD = 2 \times 16$
$$= 32 \text{ cm}$$

$AB = (42 \div 2) \times 3$
$$= 63 \text{ cm}$$

Area of $ABC = \frac{1}{2} \times 63 \times 32$
$$= 1,008 \text{ cm}^2$$

Area of $BEG = \frac{1}{2} \times 42 \times 16$
$$= 336 \text{ cm}^2$$

Shaded area $= 1,008 - 336$
$$= 672 \text{ cm}^2$$

7. Thinking skill: Spatial visualization

Strategy: Simplify the problem

Solution:

Shaded area $= \frac{1}{2} \times 12 \times 12$
$$= 72 \text{ cm}^2$$

8. Thinking skill: Spatial visualization

Strategy: Simplify the problem

Solution:

Area of 2 triangles $= 2 \times \frac{1}{2} \times 24 \times 24$
$$= 576 \text{ in.}^2$$

Area of square $= 10 \times 10 = 100 \text{ in.}^2$

Unshaded area $= 576 - 100 - 100$
$$= 376 \text{ in.}^2$$

Chapter 7

Lesson 7.1

1. 60 grams
2. 23 : 10; 11 : 60; 60 : 23; 39 : 10; 60 : 10 (or 6 : 1)
3. a. 4 : 3   b. 5 : 12
4. a. 7 : 20   b. 8 : 5
5. 14 : 15

Lesson 7.2

1. 12
2. 54
3. 56
4. 42
5. 72
6. 7
7. 9
8. 8
9. 2 : 3
10. 5 : 2
11. 7 : 4
12. 3 : 5
13. 8 : 5
14. 11 : 13
15. 2 : 3
16. 4 : 1

Lesson 7.3

1. a. 4 : 5 = 60 : 75
    He uses 75 blue tiles.
    b. 9 : 4 = 540 : 240
    He uses 240 gray tiles.

2. a. 5 : 3 = 30 : 18
    The building is 30 meters tall.
    b. 5 : 3 = 45 : 27
    The shadow will be 27 meters long.

3. 16 − 4 = 12
    18 + 3 = 21
    21 : 12 = 7 : 4

    The ratio of the number of boys to the number of girls is 7 : 4.

4. 2 units $\rightarrow$ 16 in.
    1 unit $\rightarrow$ 16 ÷ 2 = 8 in.
    Length = 5 × 8
           = 40 in.
    Width = 3 × 8
          = 24 in.
    Area of rectangle = 40 × 24
                    = 960 in.^{2}

    The area of the rectangle is 960 square inches.

Lesson 7.4

1. 8 : 5
2. $\frac{8}{5}$
3. $\frac{5}{8}$
4. $\frac{8}{13}$
5. $1\frac{3}{5}$ times
6. 3 : 8
7. $\frac{3}{8}$
8. $2\frac{2}{3}$ times
9. 77 fish

Lesson 7.5

1. 35; 20
2. 9; 18
3. 28; 36
4. 35; 63
5. 3 : 2 : 5
6. 6 : 3 : 5
7. 3 : 5 : 8
8. 4 : 7 : 8

Lesson 7.6

1. Keisha's age this year = 12 + 3
                           = 15 years

    Sarah's age : Keisha's age = 4 : 5 = 12 : 15
    Ratio in 9 years = (12 + 9) : (15 + 9)
                    = 21 : 24
                    = 7 : 8

    The ratio of Sarah's age to Keisha's age in 9 years is 7 : 8.

2. Distance Ann runs : Distance Jane runs
    = 7 : 4
    7 − 4 = 3
    12 ÷ 3 = 4 times
    4 × 7 = 28

    Jane has to run 28 meters.

3.

    10 bears
    + 5 dolls   20 bears

    4 units $\rightarrow$ 20 bears
    2 units $\rightarrow$ 10 bears
    1 unit $\rightarrow$ 5 bears
    3 units $\rightarrow$ 5 dolls

    The ratio was 3 : 1.

4. Area of P : Area of Q = 3 : 2 = 12 : 8
    Number of units for the figure
    = 12 + 8 − 5
    = 15

    Number of units for the unshaded part
    = 15 − 5
    = 10
    10 : 15 = 2 : 3

    The ratio is 2 : 3.

Put on Your Thinking Cap!

1. Thinking skill: Analyzing parts and whole

   Strategy: Use a model

   Solution:

   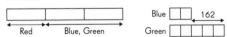

   3 units → 162
   1 unit → 162 ÷ 3 = 54
   7 units → 7 × 54 = 378
   2 units → 378
   1 unit → 378 ÷ 2 = 189
   3 units → 3 × 189 = 567

   There are 567 ribbons in the basket.

2. Thinking skill: Analyzing parts and whole

   Strategy: Use a model

   Solution:

   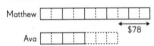

   3 units → $78
   1 unit → $78 ÷ 3 = $26
   14 units → 14 × $26 = $364

   They have $364 altogether.

3. Thinking skill: Analyzing parts and whole

   Strategy: Use a model

   Solution:

   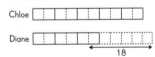

   6 units → 18
   1 unit → 18 ÷ 6 = 3
   16 units → 16 × 3 = 48

   They have 48 books altogether.

4. Thinking skill: Analyzing parts and whole

   Strategy: Use a model

   Solution:

   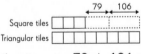

   5 units → 79 + 106 = 185
   1 unit → 185 ÷ 5 = 37
   11 units → 11 × 37 = 407

   There were 407 tiles in the box at first.

5. Thinking skill: Analyzing parts and whole

   Strategy: Use a model

   Solution:

   3 units → 261 + 261 = 522
   1 unit → 522 ÷ 3 = 174
   2 units → 2 × 174 = 348

   He had 348 apples at first.

6. Thinking skill: Analyzing parts and whole

   Strategy: Use a model

   Solution:

   a. **Method 1**

   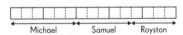

   The new ratio was 9 : 5.

   Method 2

   Andy's collection : Bobby's collection
   = 2 : 5
   = 4 : 10
   (4 + 5) : (10 − 5) = 9 : 5

   The new ratio was 9 : 5.

   b. 4 units → 108
   1 unit → 108 ÷ 4 = 27
   10 units → 10 × 27 = 270

   Bobby had 270 antique coins at first.

7. Thinking skill: Analyzing parts and whole

   Strategy: Use a model

   Solution:

   2 units → 118
   1 unit → 118 ÷ 2 = 59
   15 units → 15 × 59 = 885

   There were 885 marbles in the box.

Mid-Year Test

1.	B	2.	C	3.	C	4.	D
5.	A	6.	C	7.	B	8.	D
9.	C	10.	C	11.	A	12.	B
13.	A	14.	D	15.	A	16.	D
17.	C	18.	D	19.	D	20.	B

21. 899,300   22. 6,000

23. 84   24. 5

25. 180   26. 160

27. 78   28. $\frac{3}{4}$

29. 8   30. $\frac{2}{9}$

31. 3 : 2   32. 7

33. 13   34. 8

35. 19   36. 455

37. 540   38. 900

39. 112.5

40. Mr. Johnson drives 2 miles farther.

41.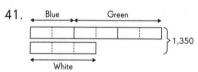

9 units → 1,350
1 unit → 1,350 ÷ 9 = 150
4 units → 4 × 150 = 600

600 green beads are used.

42. Area of triangle $BDC = \frac{1}{2} \times 12 \times 12$
$$= 72 \text{ cm}^2$$

Area of square $GEFC = 6 \times 6$
$$= 36 \text{ cm}^2$$

Area of triangle $EDF = \frac{1}{2} \times (12 + 6) \times 6$
$$= 54 \text{ cm}^2$$

Shaded area $= BDC + GEFC - EDF$
$$= 72 + 36 - 54$$
$$= 54 \text{ cm}^2$$

43.
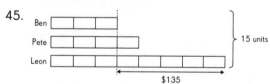

17 units → 102
1 unit → 102 ÷ 17 = 6
8 units → 8 × 6 = 48
9 units → 9 × 6 = 54

She made 48 chicken sandwiches and 54 tuna sandwiches.

44. a. Number of red balls = 48 ÷ 3
$$= 16$$

Number of white balls = 30 ÷ 5
$$= 6$$

Total number of balls = 16 + 6 + 30 + 48
$$= 100$$

There are 100 balls altogether.

b. $1 - \frac{7}{10} = \frac{3}{10}$

$\frac{3}{10} \times 100 = 30$

30 balls will be left.

45.

5 units = $135
1 unit = $135 ÷ 5 = $27
15 units = $27 × 15 = $405
They save $405 altogether.